Pearls of untold number

ENGLAND

Capt. Champaigne & goode
shippe GARGARYNE - Oct. 1569

Jan. 11 1569   Oct. 2 1567

Storm

FRANCE

ATLANTIC
OCEAN

Vigo - Dec. 3 1568

SPAIN

Azores Is.

Madeira Is.

AFRICA

...reton st.

...KE Master

...kins returneth Nov. 1568

Canary Is. Nov. 4 156...

Mar. 29 1561

Cape Verde Is.

C. Verde Nov 18 1567

Here Ingram seeth ellefants
and trumphets of Beestes teeth

...he Beeste had no necke and his
...eys and mouth were in his breast,
so sayeth DAVID INGRAM

The "Jesus of Lübeck" Capt. Hawkins' shippe

Stories for

YOUNG TEXANS

From Old Lands to New

by

J. A. RICKARD

Professor of History and Government
Texas College of Arts and Industries
Kingsville, Texas

and

CLYDE INEZ MARTIN

Associate Professor of Elementary Education
University of Texas
Austin, Texas

Illustrations by
WM. R. SOWELL
FIORE MASTRI
and
BILL NEALE

W. S. BENSON & COMPANY

Publishers   Austin, Texas

STORIES FOR YOUNG TEXANS

Books in the Series:

CALL OF THE SOUTHWEST

FROM OLD LANDS TO NEW

Printed in the United States of America

Contents

Contents

THE OPEN RANGE

THE SETTLERS CAME

MOVING ONWARD

THEN AND NOW

To Boys and Girls:

Often we forget that the New World is really an extension of the Old World. Why were men willing to risk their lives on uncharted seas and brave unknown dangers to come to a strange New World? Some came to claim new lands for their kings; others to search for gold because European nations measured their wealth in terms of gold. The need for new markets and trade routes, and the desire to convert the natives to Christianity brought still others. Adventurers and fortune hunters, also, sought every opportunity for exciting experiences.

These men brought with them ideas that were deeply rooted in Europe, plus a hope for a new land of freedom and a new beginning. Many of them came to the Southwest, where life on the frontier changed some of their ideas.

The Indians taught them about the forests, rivers, and wild animals. Old ways of traveling, obtaining food, and building shelters were changed for new ways in a new country.

The stories in this book were written and selected especially to help you understand that the roots of America lie deeply in the past. As you read them you will realize that the adventures and struggles of early settlers were the beginnings of the American way of life which we have come to know and appreciate.

We hope that you will enjoy the stories.

THE AUTHORS

Tread of the Pioneers

I hear the tread of pioneers
   Of nations yet to be;
The first low wash of waves, where soon
   Shall roll a human sea.

The rudiments of empire here
   Are plastic yet and warm;
The chaos of a mighty world
   Is rounding into form.

       — *John Greenleaf Whittier*

From Old Lands to New

The Spanish Sail Westward

The Landing of Columbus

You probably have read several stories of the landing of Columbus, but have you read one that was translated from the Spanish into the English language? The following story was translated from an old history of the West Indies.

Columbus on his first voyage discovered the West Indies which gave Spain the first claim to New World territory. It was but a short voyage from these islands to Mexico. From Mexico, the Spaniards entered Texas.

Thursday, October 11, 1492

The course was southwest, and there was a higher sea than usual. The sailors saw sandpipers and a green reed floating near the vessel. Those on the *Pinta* secured a short pole and a stick and took out of the water another small pole which had been marked with an iron tool, and they likewise found some land grass and a small board. The crew of the *Niña* (Nē′nyä) also saw signs of land and a small limb covered with berries. At these signs everyone breathed more freely and became more cheerful. Their voyage for that day was twenty-seven leagues.

After sunset Columbus set his course due west, and the ships now sailed about twelve miles an hour. By 2:00 A.M. they had sailed about ninety miles, or

22½ leagues. As the *Pinta* was a faster sailer than the one Columbus was on, and was in the lead, she first sighted land, and made the signal he had ordered her to make.

A sailor named Rodrigo de Triana (Rō drē′ gō dä Trē ä′ nä) believed he sighted land. At 10:00 P.M. the Admiral was standing on the castle of the poop. Because the night was so dim, he was not sure that he saw land; but he called Pedro Gutierrez (Pä drȯ Gōō tyä′ rȧz), the king's butler, and told him to look. He obeyed. The Admiral then called Rodrigo Sanchez (Sän′ chāz), of Segovia, whom the King and Queen had sent along as inspector and supervisor; but he, not being in a good position for observing, saw nothing. After the Admiral had talked with these men, he saw a light once or twice. It appeared to be about the size of a candle and to be rising and falling. Not many others thought that a favorable sign, but the Admiral was sure that land was close.

After they had said the *Salve* (Säl′ vä), which they were in the habit of singing and saying in their own way, the Admiral cautioned his men to keep a close watch from the forecastle for land. He promised that whoever should first see land would receive a silk doublet and an annual pension of ten thousand *maravedis* (mä rä vä dĭs), which the King and Queen had promised.

Two hours after midnight land was sighted at a distance of two leagues. All sails were lowered except a square storm sail, which is the *mainsail* without trimmings, and the ship lay at anchor till Friday near the small island of Lucayos, or *Guanahani* (Gwä nä ä′ nē), as the natives called it. The Admiral went ashore in an armed boat, taking with him Martin Alonso Pinzon and his brother Vicente Anes, who was in command of the *Niña*.

The Admiral carried the royal badges of office, and the two captains took two of the banners of the green cross bearing an *F* and a *Y*, which had been flown from all the ships. Each letter had a crown, the one being on one arm of the cross, and the other on the other arm.

On land they saw bright green trees and plenty

of water and fresh fruits of various kinds. The Admiral called on the captains and crewmen who had come ashore; and in their presence he had Rodrigo Descovedo, notary of the fleet, and Rodrigo Sanchez de Segovia to officiate. With all the others as witnesses he took possession of the island for the King and Queen, his sovereigns. . .

— *Bartholome de Las Casas*

Things to Do

1. Locate on a map of the Western Hemisphere, San Salvador, the island in the West Indies on which Columbus landed in 1492. Find the possible route that was taken later by others to Texas.
2. Make a list of the things that are mentioned in the story that you would probably see if you were to visit San Salvador today.
3. After reading the last paragraph in the story, make an illustration of the scene it describes.
4. What did the initials *F* and *Y* (or *I*) stand for? Make a list of all Spanish names and words in the story. Beside each word, write its meaning. Here is an example:
   a. Rodrigo de Triana — the sailor who first sighted land.
5. Why was Christopher Columbus's first trip to America the most important sea voyage in all history?

The First Spaniards in Texas

Castaways

The stormy sea kept pounding at the long boat in the darkness. Of the forty-one men in it, all but Cabeza de Vaca (cä bä′ zä dä vä′ cä) were too tired and weak to move. He alone kept pulling at the oars, feebly trying to guide the long vessel.

Then, above the roar of the ocean a new sound came to his ears. It was the noise of waves breaking on a beach!

Trembling with excitement, he tried to arouse his companions. "Pancho! Carlos! Land! Land!"

The two stirred, seized the oars, but the boat was out of their control. With a sudden roll it was thrown completely out of the water — up on the shore.

Thus it was that at dawn, November 6, 1528, Cabeza de Vaca and his fellow voyagers were cast ashore on Galveston Island. Wet, weak, and numb from the cold, they crawled out, made a fire, parched corn, and rested awhile. Fortunately, there was enough rain water to delight their thirsty throats.

Cabeza de Vaca turned to one of his men. "Oviedo, (ō vē ā′ dō) climb that tree and look around."

The big man obeyed the order. "We are on an island," he soon reported, "and over yonder is an Indian village."

Within an hour the Indians discovered their strange visitors and were crowding around the Spaniards, who lay exhausted on the beach. By signs Cabeza de Vaca let them know that he and his men were hungry. Nodding their heads in reply and pointing toward their village, the Indians left. They returned with roast fish and the tender roots of trees, which the Spaniards ate. In the afternoon the Indians brought more food.

Feeling stronger, the Spaniards dug their boat

out of the sand and pushed it into the water. All their food and supplies being on board, they embarked and headed for the open sea. Before they had gone a hundred yards, a large wave swept over the boat, filling it with water. A second wave overturned it. Three of the crew were drowned, and the others were washed ashore, some of them half drowned. The boat was gone, and with it all their provisions and most of their clothes.

Cabeza de Vaca reached a decision. "We must ask the Indians for more help," he said.

"We ought to get away from here," one of the men replied. "These Indians may offer us as sacrifices to their gods. The Indians of Mexico often did their prisoners that way."

"But our condition is desperate," de Vaca said. "We can't get away."

When the Indians returned later that afternoon, the Spanish leader made signs showing that he and his men wanted to be taken to shelter. The kindly Indians picked them up in their arms and carried them, stopping now and then to let them warm by the fires they had built. They lodged them in their huts and fed them more roots and roast fish.

The next day the Spaniards learned that another boatload of their countrymen had landed four miles up the beach, so they went to see about them. The whole group tried to patch up the one remaining boat, but it fell to pieces when they tried to float it. That settled things: the eighty or more men would have to spend the winter on the island. They sent four of their number down the beach to see what they could find, while the others remained behind and waited.

Their outlook was indeed dark. Two of the five boats in which they had set out from Florida in search of Mexico were now gone, and they did not know where the three others were. It was learned later, however, that a third boat had been wrecked about forty miles from the present city of Galveston. The survivors had started down the shore afoot but were overtaken by a fourth boat, commanded by Panfilo de Narváez (pän fēʹ lō dā när väʹ āz), leader of the whole expedition. Later his boat was wrecked off the coast near present-day Matagorda, and its men went to a watery grave. The fifth and last boat was also wrecked, probably near the present town of Aransas Pass.

Cabeza de Vaca and his companions did not then know the fate of the other boats; they knew only that they were helpless on an island. The larger expedition had set out from Spain by the way of the West Indies a year earlier to occupy Florida. Narváez had led about three hundred men inland on the Florida peninsula, sending his fleet ahead to wait off the coast for them. They were gone inland longer than expected; and when they returned to the coast, the fleet could not be found. They were afoot! Soon they ran out of food, and after many fights with the Indians and other hardships, they decided to leave Florida. They built five boats and set out for Mexico, little realizing that it was so far away, or that all would be wrecked in storms.

The Medicine Man

The Indians on the island were friendly with de Vaca and his men at first, but later they grew unfriendly. Perhaps they did not like the idea of having their precious food eaten by others. Certainly they did not like the terrible disease which killed half of them. Some of the Indians wanted to put the Spaniards to death, but their chief had another plan.

"You brought this disease," he told de Vaca. "Now you must cure those who are sick."

"But we do not have any magic to drive off the sickness," de Vaca answered.

"Then make some. If the whites will not heal, they shall not eat," the chief replied.

Threatened with starvation unless he did something, de Vaca decided to try. He had seen witch doctors blow their breaths on sick people and pass their hands in the air over them. He had seen priests pray for the sick and make the sign of the cross over them, and he knew a little about how Spanish doctors worked. From all these he planned a method of treatment. For some reason a few of the sick that he treated actually grew better, and this caused the Indians to spare the lives of the Spaniards.

All but fifteen of the island castaways died by early spring, and the Indians took these fifteen with them to the mainland. They went there to find berries, for they had lived all winter on a diet of roots and fish. After awhile some of the Indians returned to the island, taking with them all the Spaniards but de Vaca and one or two others who were sick and could not return until later.

On the island the Spaniards found an Indian who could be bribed to guide them, and they escaped. Only de Vaca and two other men now remained with the island Indians, and one of these soon died. The second man was the tree climber, Oviedo.

De Vaca was soon well again, but his lot was worse than ever, for now he was a slave. After a year of slavery he ran away and went to live among the Indians on the mainland, who proved to be kinder than those on the island. Oviedo stayed on the island.

De Vaca now became a trader as well as a medicine man. Often the different groups of Indians were at war and could not trade with each other, but all of them welcomed de Vaca. He went from place to place along the coast, carrying such articles as tree cones, sea shells for use as knives, and beans for eating. These he traded for animal skins, flint rock for making arrowheads, and deer sinews for bowstrings. He also carried a dye called ocher, which the Indians used to color their faces. Always he had a supply of materials for making bows and arrows.

Why did he not escape? The answer to that question is that he kept staying because he wanted to take Oviedo with him. Oviedo was the only Spaniard left on the island, and year after year de Vaca begged him to flee with him. Oviedo may have liked living with the Indians, or he may have been afraid of being killed if he were caught fleeing. Perhaps he was afraid of drowning while crossing streams, for he could not swim.

"I will go with you next year," he would tell de Vaca, but when that time came, he would refuse again to leave.

Finally, in 1534, de Vaca took Oviedo across from the island to the mainland by carrying him on

his back through the deep bay water. On the mainland they crossed four streams which later were called Oyster Creek, the Brazos River, San Bernard Creek, and Caney Creek. De Vaca took courage, for he thought his troubles were over.

However, when the two came to a stream that some historians say was the Guadalupe River, they met some Indians.

"We saw three other white men down the coast," the Indians told them. "There have been many other whites, but all except three have been killed. These three will be at this very spot in three days."

This news kept the two travelers waiting, but the Indians scared Oviedo. They threatened the white men, pointing arrows at their hearts and saying they would kill them. In spite of the pleading of de Vaca, Oviedo went back to the island. No one seems to know what finally became of him.

A few days after the departure of Oviedo, the other Spaniards came. They were Andres Dorantes (än dräs′ dō rän′ täs), Alonso Castillo (ä lōń sō cäs tē′ yō), and a Moorish Negro named Estévan (ĕs tä′ vän). De Vaca records the meeting in his writings later, saying, "We gave many thanks to God for being together again."

The Escape to Mexico

After almost seven years of wandering and suffering, the last four survivors of the Narváez Expedition were together again. They lost no time in making plans to escape.

"We had better not attempt to leave now, for the Indians are watching us," Dorantes said.

"You're right," answered de Vaca, "and they would overtake us and punish us if we tried. Our best chance will be when the pears on the cactus are ripe. All the Indians will come together then to gather them. Thus it will be easier to escape from the large crowd than at any other time."

Meanwhile, the Indians had to be kept from becoming suspicious. To avoid alarming them, de Vaca became a slave of the Indian who was already the master of Dorantes. This meant a wait of six months, for it would be that long before the pears were ripe, but the four men waited patiently.

At last the Indians set out for the cactus pear food, going to a place somewhere west of Corpus Christi Bay, perhaps near present Helena, in Karnes County. It was early in the summer of 1534 when the four Spaniards met again. Just as they were almost ready to escape, the Indians had a quarrel, and the groups broke up sooner than had been expected. Sadly, the friends parted, each one going back into slavery for another year.

Finally, another summer came and once more the Indians met to hunt food. This time the white men stole quietly away, on the road to freedom at last. Fearing they would meet unfriendly Indians if they went southwest, they started north or northwest.

They passed through the country of other Indians, but these were friendly. In some way the news had spread that these strange Europeans were healers. A short while after their start, some Indians came to them with headaches and asked to be cured. De Vaca made the sign of the cross and prayed, and the Indians declared they were well. As pay they gave venison to the four men. Other Indians came with other aches and more venison, until the four had more meat than they could eat or carry.

October of 1535 found the whites somewhere east of San Antonio. They were eager to go ahead, but the Indians discouraged them.

"Winter out there cold," one of them said. "Long way. Little food. White men better stay till spring."

De Vaca and his friends took the advice, but in the spring of 1536 they started out again. From tribe to tribe they went, performing other cures. So famous did they become that sick Indians crowded around them by the hundreds. They called the four Spaniards "Children of the Sun" and eagerly tried to get near them, or even to touch their garments, in the hope of being cured.

By that time the Europeans were in the San Antonio area, where the Indians had a village. From there they went toward the hill country west of the Austin region. It was on this part of the journey that de Vaca performed an operation. The

Indians took him a warrior with an ugly wound in his shoulder. An arrow had been buried deeply in the wound, and it "pointed toward the heart." De Vaca was told to take it out.

He hesitated. He did not mind going through the usual curing ceremony, but this was different. The only knife he had was a shell sharpened on a limestone rock, but the Indians insisted that he try. He went to work. Putting people to sleep with ether or any other anesthetic was unknown, so the warrior had to endure the pain of the cutting. De Vaca took out the arrowhead, and the man recovered. He carried the arrowhead about with him, proudly showing it, and the new "doctors" were more famous than ever.

Slowly the men went on. Not always did they have plenty to eat or friends to care for them. Once they found some Indians who themselves were hungry and could give them no food. De Vaca traded some of their skin clothing for two dogs. They ate the dogs and kept on traveling from village to village, guided always by a large escort of Indians. It is believed that they went up the Colorado to the Concho River, thence westward to the Pecos which they followed into what is now southeastern New Mexico. In his story, de Vaca relates that in this area Indians in the fall were living on game which was to be found only in valleys, and on cactus pears and piñon nuts from the pines.

They turned westward on the Rio Peñasco,

then southward; and finally, under the guidance of friendly Indians, who were familiar with trails where water and food were available, they reached the Rio Grande near the location of the present city of El Paso.

"It will be better for you to go on up the river than to cross it now," they told de Vaca. "You will get into bad country with unfriendly Indians if you cross now."

Following this advice the Spaniards did not cross the Rio Grande until they were some distance upstream where they found Indians living in fixed dwellings and growing corn, beans, and pumpkins. They were strongly tempted to seek the wonderful Seven Cities of Cíbola, about which they were hearing, but again they listened to the Indians.

"If you will now go toward the setting sun," one chieftain told them, "you will find a land of corn."

They set out to find it. In time they reached the upper part of the Sonora Valley of Mexico, where the Indians welcomed them with food. Continuing south, down the river canyon, they came to other Indians, who fed them on the hearts of deer.

Going on, the four soon found themselves in the land of the Yaqui Indians. Hanging from the neck of one Indian was a small buckle made from the head of a sword belt and was held on by a horseshoe nail. They knew then that white men had been there.

Overjoyed, the travelers continued southward.

Finally, they met some white men on horseback.
De Vaca records that "Seeing me almost naked, they
stared at me speechless; such was their surprise that

they could not find words to ask me anything. I
spoke first and asked them to lead me to their
captain."

They were now among the Spaniards of Mexico, and at the town of Culiacan (cōō lē ä căn̓)

the alcalde (äl käl′ dā) met them. After a rest they went on to Compostela, where Governor Nuño de Guzman (noō ño dā goōz män) met them and gave them clothes to wear. Again de Vaca writes, "For many days I could bear no clothing, nor could I sleep, except on a bare floor."

They reached Mexico City finally, where Viceroy Mendoza welcomed them. On July 25, 1536, the day after their arrival, there was a fiesta in honor of a saint, and it included a bullfight and a tournament. They felt at home!

And well might they so feel, for they had been wandering among the Indians more than eight years. They were the first Europeans to cross Texas. Their route had taken them from Galveston Island to Corpus Christi Bay, San Antonio, the Austin area, the Edwards Plateau, New Mexico, and El Paso, Culiacán on the Pacific coast, and to Mexico City. Historians disagree as to their exact route, but these places appear to have been on the most probable one.

It was many years before the Spanish occupied the Texas coast, but de Vaca and his companions had given them a claim to that region. The four men had learned much about the Indians also, and they had heard stories about the "northwest" which caused others to set out on exploring expeditions. One of the four, Estévan, actually went with these explorers.

De Vaca himself went back to Spain after resting awhile in Mexico City. Afterwards he wrote an account of his wanderings. Some years later he returned to the New World, going to South America as governor of a province there.

But the great work of his life had already been done. He had explored Texas.

—J. A. Rickard

Things to Do

1. This story of the early explorer of Texas, Cabeza de Vaca, may be used in several different ways by committees of your classmates. These ways are:
   a. Make an illustrated map of de Vaca's journey through Texas. Use a large outline map, discuss the route that he took, and draw pictures of events that happened along the way. Share the map with the remainder of the class by letting each member of the committee discuss events — or you might consider better ideas of your own for sharing it.
   b. Make a frieze or mural showing the journey through Texas. Underneath each scene in the frieze write a description of the event that is shown. If these stories are typed, your frieze will be much neater.
   c. Make a booklet describing the different tribes of Indians that de Vaca visited. An encyclopedia or other books about Indians would help you to learn more about each tribe than is given in the story.

2. Why did the five boatloads of Spaniards come to the Texas coast in 1528?
3. What happened to all but four of the castaways?
4. Why was Cabeza de Vaca a slave of the Indians so long?
5. Why did he become a "medicine man?"
6. Why did the Indians allow him to become a trader?
7. What were the plans that he and his three companions made to escape?
8. Why were they so long in getting away?
9. Why did the four men not escape when they were first reunited?
10. How did they finally manage to get away?
11. How did their "cures" help them to reach Mexico?
12. Why did de Vaca perform a serious operation?
13. How and where did they finally find the Spaniards of Mexico?
14. Why was their living among the Indians important?

Knight Errant of the Great Plains

The Search for the Seven Cities of Cíbola

The whole story as told by Cabeza de Vaca and his companions stirred Mexico City deeply, but the part which attracted most attention was their tale about a wonderful land to the north.

"So difficult to believe — a city paved in gold? How can you be sure?" asked the governor.

"The Indians said so! They saw it with their own eyes. And that's not all. Silver shops line the streets. The very doors of the houses are inlaid with rubies, diamonds, sapphires — all kinds of precious stones."

From person to person the story spread, and we may be sure that it lost nothing in the telling. It confirmed an old legend about a land of beautiful cities called the Seven Cities of Cíbola (sē′ bō lä). Indeed, Nuño de Gúzman, Governor of Mexico in 1530, before the arrival of Cabeza de Vaca, had sent an expedition to find them. This group turned back because they could not find a pass across the mountains, but Gúzman and other Spaniards in Mexico kept wondering about that wonderful land.

Gúzman's successor, Viceroy Antonio de Mendoza, was especially interested in the story.

"If I could discover such wealth," exclaimed he to his adviser, "I would be famous!"

"True, sire, true," confirmed his listener. "Such a prize would rival Pizarro's findings in Peru, or Cortés's discoveries in Mexico."

"Who is the man most suitable? The man to lead the expedition that would find the gold, the silver, the gems? The man who ——"

"Cabeza de Vaca, sire, has just returned."

"De Vaca! Certainly! Just the one! Fitted also is he to add converts to our church. Send for him — now —!"

But Mendoza's hopes were soon dashed to pieces. De Vaca had other plans.

"Many thanks, Governor," he replied, graciously. "Long have I been away from Spain, from

31

my family and friends that it is necessary I return. I regret I can not lead the expedition."

Hernán Cortés, conqueror of Mexico, and Hernando de Soto, later discoverer of the Mississippi River, both wanted to lead the group; but Mendoza would have neither of them. The man he finally chose was his friend Vásquez de Coronado. Going with him to spread Christianity was Friar Marcos of Nice, France.

While Coronado was preparing for the main expedition, Friar Marcos set out with a small exploring group, led by the Moorish Negro, Estévan.

When they reached uninhabited lands in northern Mexico, the Friar sent Estévan and a few Indians on ahead.

"I want you to explore the country and make peace with the Indians," he told Estévan. "And send back word of what you see. If you find a rich country, send a messenger with a cross the size of my hand. If it is a *very rich* country, send a cross twice that large. If it is richer than Mexico, send a cross still larger."

The churchman waited anxiously for the first news, and four days later it came. Two Indians returned bearing a cross "as high as a man." They also bore a message from Estévan urging Friar Marcos to follow at once. Estévan had found a new people who had told him of "the greatest country in the world." The Negro, said the messengers, was even then only thirty days' journey from the nearest of the Seven Cities of Cíbola, which was a country of wondrous wealth. Beyond the Seven Cities were other rich provinces. Greatly encouraged, the Friar set out on the second day after Easter, 1540.

Meanwhile, Estévan was traveling with all the ceremony of an Oriental monarch. He strutted, paid special attention to pretty Indian women, and issued orders in grand style. He dressed in bright robes and wore bracelets, with tufts of bright-colored feathers and strings of bells on his arms and legs. He marched across the country to the music of reed flutes, shell fifes, and fishskin drums. He carried a magic gourd decorated with bells and feathers and filled with small rocks, and sent it ahead to notify the villages of his coming. Each village was expected to furnish gifts and food for the travelers.

It was only natural that in time the Moorish leader would have trouble. When he entered the first of the Seven Cities, perhaps in present-day Arizona, or New Mexico, he was about two hundred miles ahead of Friar Marcos. The Indian leaders of that village took counsel when they heard of his demands for food and gifts.

"He is a spy, sent out by people of the south who want to conquer us," one of the Indians said.

"He is lying about the color of his masters," another Indian reasoned, "for how could he be black and they white?"

Instead of giving Estévan food and gifts, therefore, they killed him in battle. The rest of his band escaped. They fled till they met Friar Marcos. The news of the death of Estévan not only dismayed the Friar, but it scared the other Indians who were with him. They had joined him because they thought his God would protect them; but if enemies had killed Estévan, they might also kill them.

Friar Marcos tried to reassure them, but they were still afraid. In desperation he opened his bag of gifts, which he had meant to save until later.

"If you will go on with me, you may have these

gifts," he told them; so they went.

The group pushed on till they were within sight of the Indian village where Estévan had been killed. The Friar was afraid to enter it for fear that he might be slain, but he did view it from the top of a nearby hill. Perhaps a mirage gave him a distorted view, or maybe the sun gave the village a golden appearance. How it happened we cannot be certain, but Friar Marcos believed he was gazing on a city filled with riches. He took possession of the country in the name of the King of Spain and hurried back to Mexico City to tell about his discovery.

From the pulpits, on the streets, in the homes the Friar's description of the wondrous country was repeated.

"María! Listen! The Friar himself has seen the city of gold. I will return with riches untold, jewels for you, why, even silks and laces, perhaps," promised many a husband and sweetheart. In a few weeks Mendoza and Coronado had assembled a company of three hundred men to go on an expedition to Cíbola, as the fabled country was called.

It was an eager group which met at Compostela in New Galicia, the province in western Mexico of which Coronado was governor. There were Spanish nobles on horseback and with red blankets, silver-mounted bridles, and long polished lances held erect. There were foot soldiers, some with crossbows and others with guns, but all with swords and shields. There were several hundred Indians with yellow and crimson feathers on their heads and with their faces painted yellow, red, and black.

Besides the men, there were cannon, pack mules, and a thousand horses. Herds of cattle, sheep, and goats and droves of swine were driven along to serve as food. Coronado himself literally shone in bright golden armor, and beside him rode Friar Marcos in the gray robes of the Franciscan Order. Never since the days of Cortés had there been such a splendid looking army on Mexican soil.

The ceremonies for the departing army were quite in keeping with the occasion. After the group was drawn up for formal inspection, the various captains were assigned to their respective companies. A priest performed the ceremony of mass. Viceroy Mendoza made a speech, the captains and the soldiers took a solemn oath to follow and obey Coronado, and the army started off with flags flying. Viceroy Mendoza went with them for two days before turning back toward Mexico City.

All That Glitters . . .

Coronado divided his land forces. Leaving the main body at Culiacán, near the Pacific Coast, in charge of Captain Arellano (ä rā yä′ nō) with instructions to move more slowly, the leader and Friar Marcos pushed ahead with twenty-five soldiers, eighty horses, some Indians, and a few cannon. Lightly equipped, they could travel fast. Some weeks earlier Coronado had sent a dozen men ahead to explore the country again to check on Marcos's stories. Now he was looking eagerly for them, for he had told them to turn back after they had gone most of the way.

They met him and reported. Since the report of their carefully charted expedition was secret, only Coronado and Friar Marcos heard it. The men told the two they had gone more than halfway, or as far as present Southern Arizona, and had seen nothing that resembled wealth or cities. Coronado was downhearted, but Friar Marcos tried to cheer him.

"They didn't go far enough," he told the leader. "Farther on is a country where everybody's hands will be filled with something valuable, and where everything you see will be good."

Coronado wanted to believe his friend, so he resolutely kept on going. Finally, the small company came to the first of the Seven Cities of Cíbola, where Estévan had met his death and which Friar Marcos had seen from afar. The soldier Castañeda (cäs tä nyā′ dä), who was in the company and who later wrote an account of the expedition, told how the group felt when they first saw the place. He wrote, "Such were the curses that some hurled at Friar Marcos that I pray God may protect him from them."

The reason for their anger was not hard to understand. The place was not a wealthy city with streets of gold; rather it was "a little crowded village, looking as if it had been all crumpled up together." It contained approximately two hundred warriors, and its few mud-brick houses were mere huts.

The Indians in the town resisted the Spaniards and fought them. The invaders captured the city only after a hard struggle, during which Coronado himself was wounded. The Spaniards secured some needed food, but their wounded leader remained there for some time, while expeditions were sent to other parts of the country round about.

One of these set out to find a large river about which the Indians had told the Spaniards. After a journey of twenty days they reached a place where the stream literally flowed through a mountain range. The banks seemed to be ten miles across, and they were so high above the bed of the stream that the water below looked scarcely six feet wide, although the Indians had said it was a large river. The explorers spent three days looking for a path down to the stream but found none. One man went about a third of the way down, his trip taking one day. The discoverers called the river the *Tison,* or *Firebrand,* but we know now that they were seeing the Grand Canyon of the Colorado River.

They saw and heard other interesting things. Some Indians led by a man whom the Spaniards called "Whiskers" because of his long beard, told them about "cows" and showed them "birds" with large red combs. They were hearing about buffaloes and seeing turkey gobblers for the first time, and they were amazed.

This same group of Spaniards talked with an Indian who was a slave of the other Indians. He told the visitors about a wonderful place called Quivira (kē vē′ rä), his former home. The Spaniards had taken this man, whom they called the Turk, "because he looked like one," to find some of the strange hump-backed "cows" with the long hair. They became so interested in his tales about Quivira that they stopped looking for buffaloes and took him to Coronado.

To the Spanish leader the man repeated his tale and added other details. Quivira, he said contained a river that was five miles wide, and in it were fish as big as horses. On its waters were canoes so large that it took forty men to row them, and the boats had high prows of gold and white sails. The chief of that country took his afternoon naps under tall trees containing little musical bells which lulled him to sleep as the gentle breezes made them tinkle. There was so much gold in the country, continued the Turk, that even ordinary dishes were made of it, and there were many large jugs and bowls of solid gold.

It was recorded that Coronado "felt no slight joy" at such news. The snows of winter were already falling, however, and he had to wait till spring before starting in search of Quivira.

"Warm is the weather, now," declared the restless leader. "Let us set forth—the whole company. Turk, you will guide us."

They crossed the Pecos River in New Mexico and moved on to the plains of what is now called the panhandle of Texas. They saw buffaloes by the thousands and learned that they were the principal food of the Indians. A few of the Spaniards were trampled to death by the huge buffalo herds.

Again Coronado divided his forces. Sending the main group back to New Mexico, he and thirty horsemen and a few foot soldiers went on in search of Quivira.

By that time the Spanish leader was beginning to suspect that some of the Turk's stories were false, so he made a prisoner of him. The party turned north, for other Indians had said that Quivira was in that direction. Food and water became scarce, and the men began to wander about on the endless prairie. It looked so much the same, as they traveled mile after mile, that they feared they might become lost. Worse still, they feared they might die on the prairie, where their bones would bleach in the prairie sun, beside the piles of buffalo bones. They implored Coronado to turn back, but he went stubbornly on.

About thirty days after Coronado had divided his band, he and his small group crossed the Arkansas River into what is now Kansas—into the land of Quivira. Needless to say, they saw no trees with sparkling bells in them and lordly chiefs under them, nor were there any bowls of solid gold. Rather, there were crude water pitchers of pottery on the shoulders of women who had to stoop to enter the doors of the miserable, grass-covered huts. Again the historian of the expedition records, "Neither gold, nor silver, nor any trace of either, was found among these people."

Coronado turned in anger on the Turk, who confessed that he had lied to them because he wanted to be nearer his home. Furthermore, his Indian masters had promised him his freedom if he would lead the Spaniards out on the plains and

cause them to become lost, for if any should return to New Mexico after being lost, they would be so weak the Indians could kill them with little trouble. "As for gold, he did not know where there was any," were his words. Coronado then had the Turk strangled to death.

He stopped and set up a cross bearing the words, "Francisco Vásquez de Coronado, General of an expedition, reached this place." Then slowly and sorrowfully he retraced his steps across the plains and to New Mexico.

Coronado Returns to Mexico

The next spring (1542) a group of about a hundred hungry, tattered, and weary men, remnants of the once proud army of Coronado, sadly made their way back to Mexico. Their leader made a report to Viceroy Mendoza, "who did not receive him very kindly." Coronado was not publicly blamed, but he had enriched neither himself nor his king. He remained governor of the province of Galicia only a short while at which time Mendoza took the office for himself.

Everyone at the time regarded the expedition as a failure, but in reality it had accomplished much. Through it large portions of what is now Texas, New Mexico, Oklahoma, Kansas, Arizona, and Colorado had been explored. Moreover, accurate maps had been drawn and careful accounts written to guide future explorers and settlers. Since the Spanish had sent out the expedition, Spain had a good claim to the huge territory. Moreover, some of the animals in Coronado's herds escaped. They increased rapidly in the new country, providing thousands of mustangs and longhorns for future generations.

Four hundred years after the start of Coronado's expedition, that is, in 1940, those states included in the areas which Coronado had explored held a grand celebration in his honor. If he could have seen the exhibits of native products at that celebration, he might have changed his mind. He might have decided that the stories about the fabulous wealth of the country were not so untrue, after all. For those exhibits included many products of field, forest, and factory — such as plastics made from oil, clothing from cotton and wool, and gloves, boots, and shoes from hides.

— *J. A. Rickard*

Things to Do

1. Why did Viceroy Mendoza become eager to find the Seven Cities of Cíbola?
2. Why was Coronado chosen to lead the expedition?
3. Why did Friar Marcos and Estévan go ahead of the main expedition?
4. What report did Estévan send back?
5. What report did Friar Marcos make of the expedition?
6. How did the assembled company under Coronado look?
7. Why did Coronado keep on in spite of the discouraging report of the dozen men?
8. How far was the report of Friar Marcos from actual conditions in the nearest of the Seven Cities?
9. What kind of country was Quivira, according to the Turk?
10. Why did Coronado and others of his time think he had failed?
11. What evidence have we that he did not fail?
12. Divide the story into scenes for a television show; for example:
    a. Estévan's exploring group
    b. Estévan's march
    c. Coronado's army preparing to leave
13. Have committees or individuals paint each scene and write script for it.
14. Record the script with a tape recorder.
15. Arrange the pictures and script for a television show.
16. Invite another class to see the show.

The Phantom Bell

The flames from a twilight fire lighted up the narrow canyon near the foot of the mountain where the camp was pitched and revealed a strange group of travelers. Sitting to themselves were six swarthy Aztecs, and a similar group of mestizos squatted nearby. Across the fire were a dozen Spanish soldiers in full uniform, their long swords and metal trappings reflecting the fire-light. Three or four men with Spanish features and wearing the dress of adventurers, completed the group.

A silence had fallen over the company, for on the night air were sounding the clear, silvery tones of a cathedral bell. They came from the mountainside.

One of the soldiers stirred as the last peal died on the night air. "Father José and his bell," he murmured to a companion. "He watches over it like a mother watches over a sick child. Much of the time he walks beside the cart that carries it as we travel."

"And how lovingly he rings it morning and night!" added another soldier. "Always he hangs it in the woods near camp, so we can hear it. And it does have a beautiful sound."

The first soldier nodded. "Yes, one can hear

46

it many miles on a foggy morning. But think how
much trouble it has been. Already we have brought
it five hundred miles."

"And it will be another five hundred before
we stop. It's a long way from Mexico City to
Santa Fe. But the young padre was so sad that he
wept when we wanted to leave it behind."

"An odd person he is indeed—as odd as his bell,
perhaps. I wish I knew their story, but he never
offers to tell it when the time comes for stories."

"Shh!" cautioned the other soldier. "Here he
comes now. Maybe he will tell us. Who knows?"

The tall, sad-faced young padre silently took his seat by the fire near the soldiers. A momentary silence fell over the group. Finally, one of the soldiers, bolder than the others, turned to the priest.

"Father José," he said, "many are the stories that we have told at night around the fire, but always you have listened. Won't you tell us one tonight? Tell us a story about your bell."

The young padre looked startled, and a pained expression came to his face. Then he looked at the speaker and replied, "Yes, I suppose I have been selfish. You have been good to me, and you have a right to know about my bell —

"Many years ago a small village in northern Spain was inhabited by a group of fierce mountain people who were willing to fight for their liberty. Since that village was far from any other, they needed to be able to look out for themselves. Many were the enemies that they beat back.

"But alas! One day they were surrounded by an enemy that came down upon them from the north. The enemy could not conquer the brave people of the village, but they camped on all sides of it and kept out all help and food. After many days of this siege, the poor peasants faced starvation.

"At last in despair they met at the church to talk and pray. Their padre suggested that they ask the Virgin Mary to come to their aid. They promised that if she would save them, they would take all their gold, silver, and other ornaments and metals and make the finest bell that could be made.

"No one knows just what happened after that, but the village was saved — as if by a miracle. Within two hours the victorious natives were chasing the fleeing enemy into the mountains, and by night not an enemy was in sight. The camp of the foe was deserted, and his weapons were left behind.

"True to their vow, the villagers cast the bell. The leading metalsmith sent to a distant city to secure the help of another smith, and the peasants brought their metals and piled them behind the

smith's shop until the pile was higher than a man's head.

"And such a bell as it was! Its metals were so perfectly mixed that the tones were of unearthly sweetness. It was carried to the church and put in the belfry in the place of the old one. Thereafter, twice each day, and sometimes oftener, the bell rang out for the humble people of the village. It seemed to tell them of the love of the Virgin Mary, and to call down her blessings upon them.

"For many generations the bell hung in the little church of the mountain village. Each new generation told the story of its making to those who were born after them, and sometimes other stories were added. Once it was said that the bell rang of its own accord, with no sexton near it, to warn the villagers of an approaching enemy. At another time it was believed to have rung before a great storm came. The people came to think of it as their protector and friend in time of danger.

"It was to this village that I went when I first began to serve God as a padre. They were a simple, devout people, and soon I learned to love them. For several years I remained among them, and I knew such contentment as I had never known before.

"Then one day there came to my little village a messenger from the King of Spain. To my great surprise he bore a message for me. It told me that a company was being formed to go to Mexico, a land which the brave Cortés had conquered eighty years or more ago.

"In that new land, said the message, there were many people who were not Christians, and far to the north and west were places where missions should be established. I was to spend my life there working with the Indians.

"I was very sad when that message came, for I was young and full of the joy of living, and I was fond of my own country and people. I had heard of the many hardships to be suffered in the New World. Naturally I did not want to go there.

"I went with the messenger to the capital, and I even saw the king and begged him to let me stay behind. But he would not heed my pleas; indeed, he scolded me for being selfish and again commanded me to prepare for the journey.

"With a great sadness and longing in my heart for my own people, and with bitterness toward my own king, I prepared to leave my native village. The people were also sad, as we gathered for the last time in our little church, and heard the old bell ring.

"As I listened to it, it seemed to me that it was saying plainly, 'I want to go! I want to go! I want to go!' I listened and wondered if the people too could tell what it was saying.

"It must have been saying the same message to them, for finally one old man rose and pointed toward the belfry.

'We must send that bell with Father José as a blessing from his people,' said the old man in a trembling voice.

"It was packed carefully and carried to the port. For awhile I thought the captain of the ship would not let it go, but I begged for it. In the end he let me take it, just as you have let me bring it on this journey from Mexico City. And that is why I love it so much."

There was dead silence in the camp after Father José had finished his story. For several minutes nobody even stirred. Finally, someone noticed that the fire was burning out, and someone else remarked that it was time to go to sleep. When the travelers began to stir, they noticed that the padre was no longer with them.

But that was not strange, for he often spent much time in the woods alone or with his bell. Thus, when they heard it give four or five peals, they knew he was with it. It brought peace to their weary bodies and minds, and they slept soundly.

Since no one stayed awake, none knew that Father José did not return. Presently the wind began to blow, and clouds covered the sky. A great blackness appeared in the west, from which lightning flashed and thunder rumbled. The men had experienced such night storms before, and now they hurried to stake down their tents and cover their food and other articles to keep them from getting wet. Still no one noticed that Father José was absent.

As the first drops of rain began to fall, the faint sound of a bell was heard. Its tones were those of the bell of Father José, but it seemed to be on the mountain top and far away, instead of near them, as it had been. The faster the rain fell, the faster and louder came the tones of the bell, until it seemed as if it were calling them to come.

At last some of the men decided to brave the rain and storm to look for Father José, even though it was still dark, for they were beginning to fear that some ill might befall him.

By the time the men were ready to start their search, the rain had stopped; and before that, the sounds of the bell had ceased. There had been a blinding flash of lightning, followed by a loud clap of thunder, and after that the bell had rung no more.

In the mud and darkness the searchers made their way up the mountainside to the spot where they thought the bell was hung, but they could not find it. Some of them went farther, and they spread out both to the east and to the west. For an hour or more they searched. They called his name, but he did not answer. Even after they had returned to their camp, some of them sat up the rest of the night, hoping to see him come in; but he did not come.

The next morning all the men in the expedition turned out to form a searching party. They looked all over the top and sides of the mountain, and they looked for footprints along the banks of the Rio Grande nearby, but not a trace of the bell or of the padre could they find. They had completely disappeared from the earth.

And they never did learn what became of the lost man of God and his bell. After spending three days on the spot vainly looking and hoping to find some trace of them, the party slowly took up their journey again toward the new mission of Santa Fe.

The men of the group did not agree on what had happened to Father José and his bell. As people were somewhat superstitious in those days, some said that they had been changed into spirits and had flown away in the night. Others believed that the bell was a spirit which the Virgin Mary had sent to earth to protect Father José, and that when he could not bear the loneliness any longer, it carried him to heaven. Some of the party found footprints, but the rain had washed most of them out, so that no one could tell which way they led.

A number of the group, including the captain, reasoned that Father José must have hung his bell in an arroyo, and that when it was filled with water from the rain, the tree was washed into the Rio Grande, taking both the man and the bell with it.

But no body was ever recovered, and no bell was ever found anywhere down the river.

Today among the natives of the upper Rio Grande and the mountains of southern New Mexico, are many people who believe that they have heard the tolling of a spirit bell since then. At night or during a rain storm they sometimes catch the sleeve of a stranger in excitement and mutter, "There it is! The phantom bell is ringing!"

On damp foggy mornings, also, the faint but distinct tones of a bell may sometimes be heard echoing across valleys or among hills. Some dismiss such experiences by saying that the sound comes from a bell on the neck of a goat, but the native believes it is the phantom bell.

So the legend lives on, but it has bases of truth, for there was really a Father José, and he did have a bell that he was taking to the missions in New Mexico, and they did disappear never to be found again. All this is told in the matter-of-fact reports of the captain who led the expedition.

— *J. A. Rickard*

Things to Do

1. Tell how the following words or phrases are used in the story to arouse feeling, such as sympathy, sorrow, regret:

a. silence fell over the group
b. silvery tones
c. lovingly rings it
d. a foggy morning
e. startled
f. in despair they met at the church
g. victorious natives
h. a simple, devout people
i. with great sadness and longing in my heart
j. a great blackness appeared
k. heard the tolling of a spirit bell

2. What bases of truth are there in the story?

3. What do you think happened to the padre and his bell?

San José Mission

The Sculptor of San José Mission

The main entrance near the bell tower of the San José Mission in San Antonio is noted for its beautiful façade. From far and near artists have come to see it, and with one accord they have pronounced it one of the finest pieces of sculpture in the New World. Though defaced by more than two centuries of weather and by many a thoughtless souvenir hunter, it is a marvel still. After looking at it, one naturally turns to the modest grave not far away, where lie the remains of the artist who created the work: Juan Huisar (Wē sär).

There is a story about this man, a story that has several versions. Thus we may not be sure about the truth of its every detail. Of one thing, however, we can be certain: this, his greatest work, was produced as a result of a great sorrow. On that, all the stories are agreed.

Juan Huisar was a native of Old Spain and the son of a great artist. His parents gave him the best training possible, because at an early age he showed much talent for sculpture. His own father taught him first, after which Juan studied under other prominent artists in Spain. Finally, he completed his training by studying in Italy, then the home of the world's greatest sculptors. When his instruction

was complete, he returned home to practice his profession.

He had hardly begun working when he met and fell in love with the beautiful Ines de Loja. She returned his affection, but one big obstacle had to be overcome before he could claim her for his bride: he was poor, and she was rich. Given time, he too might become wealthy working at his profession, but of this there could be no assurance. Certainly her parents would not let their only daughter marry a poor, struggling, unknown sculptor.

He could see but one way to remedy this matter: to seek his fortune in the New World. Fortunes were being made there in the early eighteenth century, as the lovers well knew. Though it might mean several years of waiting and separation, the delay would make their reunion all the sweeter.

Accordingly, Juan tearfully parted from his sweetheart and sailed for the New World. In time he arrived at the site of present San Antonio. Just as he was making final plans to go on a treasure-hunting expedition with a group of other adventurers, he received a message from the King of Spain.

Borne by recent post, this message notified him that his king wanted him to return home. Talented sculptors were needed in Spain, wrote the king, and a liberal pension for life would be paid Juan if he would accept the offer. Moreover, he could sail for Spain on the same ship that had carried the king's letter to him.

Juan could not wait. He hurried to the port of Matagorda Bay, where he hoped that even before sailing time he might see some acquaintance among the new arrivals from Spain who could bring him late news from Ines.

Suddenly one day he saw the familiar face of an old friend from whom he eagerly begged news from home. The man became nervous. He tried to talk about other things, but Juan pressed him for information. Finally he turned; and putting one hand on Juan's shoulder, said as gently as he could, "You might as well hear the truth. Your sweetheart has married another man. She did not wait for you."

Heavy hearted, Juan slowly journeyed back to San Antonio. No longer did he wish to go home; in fact, he did not know where he wanted to go. In desperation he confided his troubles to a kindly old padre who was sympathetic.

"I, too, suffered such a blow when I was young," he said, "and the only remedy I found was work. You will find it the same. They are building a mission at Bexar, and they need a man of your ability. Go there and work for God."

Juan went, and he worked. For more than ten years he toiled with chisel and hammer. Into his labors he poured his feelings until the façade of the San José Mission grew into a work of art, a marvel to behold.

However, if we are to believe the stories, he did not find in it an end to his sorrow. In those years of disappointment and long hours of work he rapidly became an old man, and his health failed. He clung to his tools, however, barely laying them down long enough to eat and sleep. Even in his final illness he begged to be allowed to keep working.

Over his last resting place, near where he worked, has been placed a small model of the mission on which he labored so faithfully, and at the head of his grave is a monument to his memory. Though he failed to gain happiness for himself, he bestowed it on others through his sacrifice.

— *J. A. Rickard*

Things to Do

1. Artists have said that the façade of San José Mission is one of the most beautiful in the world. Have you seen it?
2. After reading the story, you should be able to discuss the following statement:
   When we fail to get something that we want very much, other things may bring us peace and happiness.
3. What might have been the outcome of Juan Huisar's life if he had gone back to Spain and married Ines?

The English Sail Westward

The First Englishmen in Texas

The waves were so high and the sea so rough that the sixteenth century sailing vessel, though anchored, threatened to overturn. On the nearby shore were more than two hundred men. They could see the English flag at mast and its large letters spelling out the word M I N I O N.

None paid much attention to the rocking, rolling ship, for they were clustered about Captain John Hawkins, who was addressing them — about half the total company.

"All right, men, I have granted your request and put you ashore. I'm thinking it's an unwise choice. You'll be at the mercy of savage Indians or uncivilized Spaniards."

One of the men replied, "Aye, Captain, but full well you know your ship is overloaded and under-provisioned. All of us could never make it to England in that vessel. Chances are we would all be lost at sea."

"That's true," admitted Hawkins, "yet I dread to set my own countrymen ashore among enemies. But I suppose it's best. You're right—if we all attempt to cross the Atlantic in yonder ship, we risk

drowning at sea or being reduced to eating one another to keep from starving. Well, men, God be with you till we meet again!" Having thus spoken, the captain set out in a small boat for his vessel.

The 114 men left ashore elected one of their number, Miles Phillips,[1] leader and took stock of

---

[1]Later, Miles Phillips, who went south with Anthony Goddard and was captured by the Spaniards and taken to Mexico City, wrote his story of suffering there. For fifteen years he was a captive, but finally escaped and made his way back to England. His report confirms that portion of Ingram's story before their separation. Also Job Hortop, in the same group, was made a galley slave and, after 28 years, escaped, returned to England and made a written report of his adventures. (See Hakluyt's *Voyages and Discoveries of the English Nation*)

their slender supplies of food and arms. Remnants of a fleet of six vessels that had entered Vera Cruz harbor on September 16, 1568, they knew they were about thirty miles north of present Tampico, Mexico, and that enemies were all around them. The Spanish had allowed their fleet to cast anchor in the harbor, but seven days later they attacked their visitors, after having solemnly promised to be friendly.

The Spanish excuses for this action may have been valid in part. Perhaps the Englishmen were corsairs and pillagers of other vessels on the high seas. Certainly they were slave traders who had sold their cargoes of "black ivory" at Spanish ports in violation of the law. They were also Protestants, or "heretics," and members of a nation with which Spain was virtually at war. Regardless of these facts, the Spanish action was a serious breach of faith, and the condition of the exiled Englishmen was far from promising.

The next few days brought more disasters. Three men had drowned in the landing. The next day as they wandered along the shore, the Indians attacked and killed eight more. They captured the whole party, stripped them of their clothing, and grunted in amazement at their white bodies. Then the captors pointed toward Tampico and left them naked and helpless.

The survivors divided into two groups. One, under the command of Anthony Goddard, decided

to go south. In that direction they knew they would
find the Spanish enemy, but at least they would
have food, along with their imprisonment. And
perhaps the Spaniards would not mistreat them too
much.

The other group, of about equal size, turned
north, preferring the hazards of an unknown country to facing the armed Spaniards again. Two days
later the Indians once more attacked them, this
time slaying their leader and two more of their
company. This was too much for most of them.
Twenty-five or thirty of them turned back, joined
the Goddard party four days later, and went on
south with them. They continued until they met
the Spaniards and were taken prisoners. Eventually

they were sent to Mexico City, where they were delivered to the Court of the Inquisition to be punished as heretics.

Of the twenty-odd men left, all but three soon disappeared. These were David Ingram, Richard Brown, and Richard Twide. What became of the others is not known. Perhaps they followed their companions south; certainly they did not continue to the north.

The journey of these three men is one of the most remarkable in all history, since they traveled afoot for twelve months in an unknown, uncharted, savage country, their lives in constant danger. For resourcefulness, courage, and endurance, it has only one known equal: that of Cabeza de Vaca, shipwrecked on Galveston Island in 1528 — just forty years earlier[1]. After lingering for some time in Mexico, Ingram and companions crossed the present-day Rio Grande, which they called the River of May. Then they made their way up the Texas Gulf coast, keeping almost in sight of the Gulf waters as they traveled. In due time they crossed the Mississippi River. Leaving the Florida peninsula to their south and right, they proceeded up the Atlantic coast. No English colonies had been established at that time, but they crossed territory now known as

_____

[1]This amazing journey across America, the full length of the United States from south to north and more, is comparable in many respects to the equally amazing journey from east to west, made by the Spaniard Cabeza de Vaca and his companions some thirty years earlier. —DeGolyer's *Across Aboriginal America—Journey of Three Englishmen Across Texas,* 1952.

the southern states, and also Delaware, Pennsylvania, New York, and New England. Finally, at the St. John River, Cape Breton, they were picked up by a French vessel, the *Gargarine*, commanded by Captain Champaigne.

This was in October, 1569, almost exactly a year from the time of their departure from Mexico. They were taken to Havre, France, and from there in due time they made their way to their native home, England.

Of course, they told tales about their travels, for their voyage had first led them to the Azores, Africa, South America, and other parts of the world. But the strangest of all their stories were their experiences on the River May and their year-long trip through savage America.

News of their travels finally reached the ears of Sir Walter Raleigh and his half-brother, Sir Humphrey Gilbert, the famous explorer. As Gilbert himself was preparing to make a voyage to the New World, America, he talked to the men. After some persuading, he induced Ingram to tell the full story of their journey through Texas and the rest of the New World. A scribe took down the words of Ingram's account, in this way preserving it.

The Ingram story was published in the first edition of Hakluyt's *The Principal Navigations, Voyages, and Discoveries of the English Nation, 1589*. It was omitted from later editions of the book because it was feared that the story was overdrawn.

Indeed, there are some "tall" tales in Ingram's story, or possibly he became confused in some of his descriptions. His imagination might have been helping when he told about "a strange Beeste, bigger than a Beare, that had neither head nor neck: his mouth and eyes were in his breast." Yet it is probable that he was describing a buffalo.

He told also of the bread of the root called cassava and the tree called plantine, "with the fruit growing on it like a pudding, which is most excellent eaten raw." Probably he was describing the Irish potato and the papaya. Those parts of his story which mention rubies four inches long, and white teeth dug from marshes, which smelled as sweet as musk are probable overstatements. If they were, he may be pardoned, for doubtless Sir Humphrey wanted to hear a good story, and Ingram was willing to oblige him.

But it has been proved beyond a doubt that Ingram was a member of a landing party which went northeast after having been put ashore near Tampico, Mexico, by Captain John Hawkins. Incidentally, Hawkins's partner, Francis Drake, apparently was in command of the other ship which escaped. He spent much of the rest of his life preying upon Spanish commerce in return, so he said, for the treachery of the Spanish in attacking the English corsairs after promising not to do so.

There can be no doubt that some twelve months later three ragged and miserable men of the Hawkins

Ingram, Twide, and Browne receiving rewards for their sufferings from Captain John Hawkins after their return to England.

expedition were picked up far north on the Atlantic coast line by a French ship. These same men hunted up their old captain after returning to England, and Hawkins gave to each man a sum of money to pay him in part for his sufferings.

Moreover, in spite of exaggerations by Ingram about the fearful animals and marvelous plants that he and his companions saw, he shows a knowledge of the country that could have been gained only by having seen and passed through it. It was—and still is—common to "add to" a story of adventure. Ingram yielded to the temptation. So long as he was telling a yarn, he might as well tell a good one. His story, therefore, is a curious mixture of facts and fancies, but the facts are there, fully evident, if one will look for them.

Certainly he showed a first-hand knowledge of Texas. The "River of May," which unquestionably was our Rio Grande, was set in the midst of a country "most excellent, fertile, and pleasant, especially towards the River of May, for the grass of the prairies is not so greene, as it is in these parts, for the other is burned away with the heat of the Sunne."

His description goes on to include the Rio Grande Valley and other portions of the Texas Gulf area over which the three men traveled. He continues: "And as all the Countrey is good and most delicate, having great plaines, as large and as fayre in many places as may be seene, being as plaine as a board."

Mentioning several kinds of trees which he found, paying special attention to the palm tree, he says, "The Palme trees aforesaid, carieth haires on the leaves thereof, which reach to the ground. Whereof the Indians doe make ropes and cords for their cotten beds, and doe use the same for many other purposes."

On that subject he continues, "The which Tree, if you pricke with your knife, about two foote from the roote, it will yeelde a Wine in colour like whey, but in taste strong. . .which is most excellent drinke. But it will distemper both your head and your body, if you drink too much thereof, as our strong Wines doe in these parts." Evidently Ingram had a personal knowledge of the strength of one of the Mexican drinks, pulque or tequila.

He has other things to say about the palm tree. "The branches of the top of this tree are most excellent meat raw, after you have pared away the bark. Also there is a red oyle that cometh out of the root of this tree, which is most excellent against poisoned arrows and weapons: for by it they doe recover themselves of their profound wounds." Just how valuable this oil really was for the cure of wounds is uncertain, but the Indians believed it had curative effects.

In another part of his account Ingram described a red berry, "two or three inches long, which groweth on short bushes full of pricks, and the fruit eateth like a green raisin, but sharper somewhat. They stamp this berry and make wine thereof, which they keep in vessels made of wood." Allowing for some exaggeration in the "two or three inches" part of the story, this would be a very good description of an old fashioned dewberry, or perhaps, a blackberry patch somewhere in East Texas.

Near that same description is another which shows a knowledge of the wild Texas mustang grape, for he says, "They have also in many places Vines which bear grapes as big as a man's thumb."

The birds and fowls of the country through which he went attracted the attention of Ingram.

Somewhere along the way, probably in Mexico, he came across "an abundance of russet parrots, but very few greene." He mentioned also, a "great plentie of Guinie hennes, which are tame birds, and proper to the inhabitants." He also listed, "a bird called a Flamingo, whose feathers are very red, and is bigger than a Goose, billed like a shovell, and is very good meate." He may be a bit confused in his description, but evidently he saw a bird called by that name today.

One of the most interesting and convincing of his descriptions, however, is of "a very strange Bird,

thrice as big as an eagle, very beautiful to beholde: his feathers are more ornamental than a Peacocke's feathers, his eyes are glittering as Hawke's eyes but as great as a man's eyes—He hath a crest and tuft of feathers of funny colours on top of the head like a Lapwing hanging backwards: his beaks and talents in proportion like eagles, but very huge and large." Does he not describe our turkey, which is so popular at Thanksgiving and Christmas?

His description of Texas storms, or perhaps of storms farther east or north—for he does not say exactly where he saw them on his journey—is given in this way: "Touching Tempests and other strange monstrous things in those partes, the traveler sayeth that he hath seene it Lighten and Thunder in sommer season by the space of foure and twenty houres together: the cause whereof he judgeth to be the heat of the climate.

"He further sayeth that there is a Cloud sometime of the yeere seene in the skye, which commonly turneth to great Tempests, and that sometimes of the yeere there are great winds in the manner of Whirlwinds." Again, our traveler must have been through some real Texas weather, including a tornado.

Although Ingram and his companions did not stay more than seven days in any one place, they learned much about the Indians. Ingram told how they lived, how they were governed, and what religious beliefs they held. In political matters he called their chiefs "kings." He said there were many

kings, commonly from a hundred to a hundred twenty miles apart, and that they were always at war with each other. They wore painted or colored garments, were adorned with precious stones, and were carried about publicly in ornamented chairs garnished with precious stones. Approaching such a leader was quite a ceremonious task involving kneeling and rising again. The king's right-hand men wore on their heads feathers "of a Byrde as big as the Goose and of russet colour."

Ingram described the people as being "naturally

very courteous, if you do not abuse them, either in their persons or goods, but use them courteously." He learned how to bargain with them, explaining that process in these words: "If you will bargaine for ware with them, leave the thing that you will sell upon the ground and go from it a pretty way off. Then will they come and take it, and set down such wares as they will give for it in the place. And if you think it is not sufficient, leave the wares with signes that you like it not, and they will bring more until either they or you be satisfied, or will give no more. Otherwise you may hang your wares upon a long pole's end, and so put more or less on it, until you have agreed on the bargain."

Some of the natives with whom Ingram came into contact were lovers of music, for they had trumpets made of the teeth of certain beasts, and drums made of the skins of beasts. They also had shields and targets of the skins of beasts, put together with yellow twigs, and dried. They had darts, headed with stones, the heads being two fingers broad and half a foot long, fastened within a socket. They likewise had bows and arrows, short, broad knives of black stone about a yard long, and stone knives, "wherewith they carve excellently both in wood and bone."

In religious affairs, Ingram said some of the Indians had for their god a devil, called Colluchio, "who speaketh to them sometimes in the likeness of a blacke Dogge, and sometimes in the likeness of a black Calfe." Some of them worshiped the sun, moon, and stars.

Such, in brief, was the account of this Englishman as he and his two friends made their journey through the wilds of present-day Mexico, Texas, and the United States in 1568 and 1569. Not many histories even mention their miraculous adventure, but it deserves more attention than it has received.

Nor were the results of that voyage without value. Texas was not settled immediately afterward, it is true, but explorations of the Atlantic coast were made, and English colonization was begun at Roanoke Island, Jamestown, and Plymouth Rock. Sir Humphrey Gilbert did make his journey, and although he failed in his attempted settlement, others after him succeeded. The information which Ingram passed on to Hawkins, Gilbert, Raleigh, and others was extremely valuable to the English.

— *J. A. Rickard*

Jesus de Lubeck, Flagship of Captain John Hawkins.

Things to Do

1. Why did the men from Captain John Hawkins's ship request to be left on the wild shores of Mexico? What were the dangers that they faced?
2. What finally became of most of the men and who were the remaining three?
3. Use a map of the United States and trace Ingram's journey as it is described in the story.
4. Who was Sir Humphrey Gilbert and why was he interested in Ingram's stories?
5. How was the difficult journey of these three Englishmen helpful to English colonizers?
6. Read aloud the stories that Ingram told that are possibly "tall" tales. Give your reasons for thinking that these stories may not be true.
7. Choose from the story the tales that probably can be proved. Read these aloud to your class.
8. In what ways was Ingram's journey like the experiences of Cabeza de Vaca?

English Colonizers in America

Sir Walter Raleigh has been called the father of English colonization in America. It is true that he and his half-brother, Sir Humphrey Gilbert, established the first English colony at Roanoke Island, North Carolina. From this beginning there was rapid colonization by the English in Virginia, in New England, and elsewhere. Then English-speaking peoples gradually colonized the entire South and West, including Texas.

After Roanoke Island, Raleigh sailed to Panama and to the Caribbean. On the Orinoco River, off the Caribbean Sea, he established a colony, and it was there that his son lost his life in battle with the Spanish.

In the spring of 1583 there was a hustle and bustle at the old home of the Gilberts in southern England. Gaily dressed courtiers had gathered, for they were expecting a visit from Queen Elizabeth. There were grave elders, their beards carefully trimmed; young cavaliers in rich velvets and long plumes; and women both old and young, all looking their dainty best. The finest looking man, perhaps, was a tall, handsome cavalier about thirty years of age.

Presently the queen appeared. In due time she and some others set out for a walk in the park near the castle. It had rained, and pools of water had collected in places along the walk. The queen stopped in front of a muddy place and looked with dismay at her dainty shoes. The handsome man, Sir Walter Raleigh, stepped forward and flung his beautiful velvet coat in the mud in front of his sovereign.

She smiled at him gratefully and went on, but thereafter she remembered him. The two became good friends, and she gave him large estates both in England and in Ireland.

Sir Walter was not only handsome and polite, but he was well educated and studious. Almost a century had passed since the English explorer, John Cabot, had discovered in 1497 the mainland of North America and had given England a claim to it. Yet in all this long period, the English had not been successful in colonizing the new land. A short time before this, Raleigh's half brother, Sir Humphrey Gilbert, had attempted a settlement in Newfoundland, but it had failed. His colonists refused to stay in the New World, and on the way home their ship was sunk in a storm, and all on board were lost.

However, Raleigh was not discouraged at the sad death of his brother. He now asked the consent of the queen to establish a colony, or settlement, in America. She smilingly gave her permission and furnished him with a written permit, or charter, to govern the new colony.

At his own expense he prepared two ships for visiting America to select a suitable place for his colony. He did not go on this first voyage, for the queen would not allow her new friend to risk his life in an unknown sea. His ships reached a spot on the eastern coast of present-day North Carolina, and the colonists liked the country very much. They reported the finding of an abundance of grapes, sweet-smelling trees, many song birds, and friendly natives. To prove that the country was valuable, they carried back a cargo of furs and wood.

Both Raleigh and Queen Elizabeth were so delighted with this report that they named the country Virginia, in honor of the unmarried or the Virgin Queen, as she was often called. With her aid, Raleigh fitted out an expedition of seven ships and more than one hundred colonists. In due time they reached the New World and settled on Roanoke Island, near where the ships had visited the year before.

But they were not at that time successful colonists. Instead of working the land and raising their own food, they paid too much attention to looking for gold, which they did not find. They were not skillful in their treatment of the Indians who became unfriendly and threatened to attack them. They became so discouraged that when a fleet of English ships stopped by their settlement, they deserted it to return to England.

But Raleigh was not ready to give up. The very next year, he sent out another group of colonists led by a man named White. They occupied the houses that the earlier colonists had built and deserted on Roanoke Island. Soon after their landing, a baby was born to one family, and she was named Virginia Dare. She was the first English child born in America.

A short time later the leader, Governor White, went back to England for supplies. Because he found England and Spain at war, he did not return

for three years. When he did, he could find no
trace of his granddaughter, Virginia Dare, her parents,
or any of the other colonists. No one knows to this
day what became of them.

Raleigh had spent so much money on these two
ventures that he could not finance another colony.
Besides assisting in starting a colony Raleigh carried
back to England the leaves of a weed found in the
New World. The Indians rolled them up and
smoked them. The Englishmen who did likewise
declared that the weed made them less tired and

hungry. Raleigh gave some of the broad leaves to the queen and others. Soon smoking became popular in England. The colonists also brought back a root which the Indians called the "botah." Raleigh planted some of these roots in Ireland, where they grew well. Soon the "Irish potato" was popular there.

Later, Raleigh made other attempts at colonization. He fitted out expeditions to Panama, the Caribbean Sea, and the northern coast of South America, where Spanish vessels had been going to search for gold. This time he went along himself, but he found none.

Meanwhile his friend, Queen Elizabeth, had died. The next ruler of England, James I, disliked Raleigh because he thought the cavalier had tried to prevent him from becoming king.

Raleigh was imprisoned, tried for treason, and sentenced to death. For twelve years he was kept in prison; then he was released and allowed to make another voyage to South America in search of gold. It was an important voyage for him, for he knew that if he succeeded he would probably be freed. But if he failed, he would probably die. He not only found no gold, his young son who had gone with him, was killed. The broken-hearted old man returned to England, where he was again imprisoned. Shortly afterward he was put to death.

It would seem that much of his life had been a failure, for he had established no permanent colonies and found no gold. But he did arouse English interest in the New World and added to the information concerning it. He gave to his countrymen a knowledge of tobacco and the Irish potato; also, he gave the name of Virginia to a land that later became the first English settlement in North America. He also aroused English interest in Latin America, Texas being a part of Spanish territory at the time. For these reasons, Texans should know about Raleigh and his work.

— J. A. Rickard

Things to Do

1. The story of Sir Walter Raleigh's first meeting with Queen Elizabeth is well-known. Choose two persons to dramatize it.
2. How did the queen help Raleigh afterward?
3. Why did the first two attempts to establish colonies in America fail? Read aloud the answers from the story.
4. What were the products that the English colonists brought back to England?
5. Read the descriptions of Raleigh's last two voyages to South America. Why were these voyages important?
6. Raleigh has been called the "father of English colonization in the New World." Tell why you would agree or disagree.

The French Sail Westward

The First Frenchmen in Texas

A sailing vessel flying the French flag cast anchor in the St. Lawrence River near the little town of Montreal the summer of 1666. Rene-Robert Cavalier, (rē nā′ rō bâr′ kä väl yē′), twenty-three years of age, strode down the gangplank to the dock. There his Jesuit brother Jean (zhän) greeted him.

"I am glad to see you, even though you do not

come in the garb of a churchman," Jean said after the first greetings.

"My parents were disappointed also," the newcomer admitted, "for they educated me to be a priest. But now, surprisingly, I am looking for land and a fortune."

"The land is here, certainly. New France has a promising future, although life is not as pleasant here as it is in France. However, I'll help you get settled."

This Jean did. Shortly after their reunion, a large tract of land was given to Rene-Robert, whose title was really Seigneur de la Salle, (sān' yĕr dĕ là sȧl'), better known as La Salle. The colonists whom he helped to settle on his land worked for him in return for his efforts. Soon he was regarded as one of the most prominent men in the French New World colony.

Many people would have been satisfied with such a life, but La Salle wanted to travel. He had heard of a great river "flowing into the sea," a river reached only by making a long journey. The Indians called it the Mississippi, or "Father of Waters." La Salle believed it flowed into the Pacific Ocean or "South Sea." In those days, when no one knew how broad North America was, many people believed there was a water passage across it. If they could only find this passage, they said among themselves, they could sail on to the Far East, as Columbus had tried to do.

Deciding to become an explorer, La Salle sold his land in Canada, and one July day in 1669 he started up the St. Lawrence River with twenty-three men. They had nine canoes and were equipped for a long journey.

That was the beginning of eleven years of exploration. On this particular trip he probably reached the Ohio and Illinois rivers, but not the Mississippi. Later he established a home on Lake Ontario at a place called Fort Frontenac, where he lived several years and prospered in fur trading.

But he still wanted to go to the mouth of the

Mississippi. Finally, on April 9, 1682, his long ambition was realized. After sailing many hundreds of miles down a deep river with flower-covered banks and moss-decked trees, the adventurers approached the place where it spread far out on each side and flowed lazily toward the vast expanse of water ahead. All hands were on deck, watching, lost in wonderment.

Suddenly, a sailor broke the spell, "An ocean! Or — a sea? A gulf?" Loud laughter followed.

"Correct, Pierre! (pē ẽr´). An ocean, mayhap, or a sea, or a gulf. What matter which it be? Before us lies the fulfillment of our dreams. Here the great river, the Father of Waters, the Mississippi, flows to the sea . . . . Prepare to cast anchor!"

Amid cries of joy, thankful prayers, and shouts of "Long live the King," La Salle and his men put ashore. At the landing place he erected a marker on which he wrote, "Louis the Great reigns; April 9, 1682." To make the event all the more formal, he solemnly declared, in the presence of his men and of some watching Indians, "Henceforth, my God and my King, supreme forever, over the numberless souls and the unmeasurable lands of this great continent."

At once there came to his mind a daring project — to found a city at the mouth of the great river. "On this spot will some day be the largest city in the New World," he predicted, and he set out to make his plans come to pass.

He hurried back to Canada, as New France was also called, and took the next sailing ship for France. As soon as possible he saw King Louis XIV. To the monarch he painted a glowing word picture — of a country rich in resources, of a mighty river flowing into the Gulf, and of an empire greater than any which France then owned. But Louis XIV was not fully convinced.

"Spain has colonies close by," he objected. "Her rulers might not like it."

"I propose to establish a fort and a city at the mouth of the river," La Salle replied. "That would be a natural outlet for our colonies in the north, and it would also keep the Spanish from claiming these lands."

When the king still hesitated, La Salle added, "And is it not a good idea, while we are at peace with Spain, to found a seaport somewhere in the Gulf of Mexico? We may soon be at war with them, and such a base would help us."

The king was finally convinced. He permitted La Salle to enlist two hundred soldiers and furnished him four ships. One, the *Joly*, was a ship of thirty-six tons from the French Navy. Another was the *Amiable*, a six-gun ship. Two other smaller vessels, the *Belle* and the *St. Francis*, completed the group.

In addition to the soldiers, some of whom were eager to leave France because of criminal records, were thirty "gentlemen" from the highest French social class. Other interesting people included pilots, mechanics, laborers, and six or seven priests, as well as several families with marriageable daughters. Quantities of food and ammunition; articles for trade with the Indians; and supplies for a blacksmith shop and a chapel that would be needed by the future colonists were also loaded on the ships.

The group started from France late in July, 1684, but the *Joly* met with an accident and had to go back for repairs. It was August before they were under way again.

La Salle had asked for full control of the expedition, but the king commissioned Captain Beaujeu to command not only the largest ship, the *Joly*, but also the entire voyage. The passage was dangerous, and the sea rough. La Salle and Beaujeu quarrelled.

It is not surprising, then, that misfortune beset the group from the first. The *St. Francis*, being slower than the others, fell behind, and a Spanish ship captured it. While delayed in the West Indies, La Salle lay desperately ill for several weeks.

The ships finally entered the Gulf of Mexico, but they sailed too far to the south, missing thereby the mouth of the Mississippi, where La Salle had intended to land. Farther and farther west they went down the coast, looking for the mouth of the great river but not finding it. Meanwhile, discontent was spreading among the crew and the passengers.

At last an opening appeared in the coast line, and muddy water was flowing through it. "The Mississippi at last!" La Salle exclaimed, but he soon learned that he was mistaken. Because of sand bars, he could not even harbor his ships. There was nothing to do but to keep sailing west.

As the group moved on down the coast, they noticed broad prairies and grassy expanses. The Mississippi region had not looked like that. Slowly they turned back east and entered Pass Cavallo, on the west side of San Bernardo or Matagorda Bay.

"Perhaps this is the Mississippi River," La Salle said. He sent some men to explore the country, while others made camp on present-day Matagorda Island.

They had not been there long before Indians captured some of the men. As La Salle and others went to rescue them, they heard the deafening boom of cannon. Looking back, they saw that smoke was coming from the guns of the ship *Amiable*.

"She's in trouble! She's run aground!" one of the men in the party shouted.

Luckily for the prisoners, the cannon shots had scared the Indians so badly that they had fled,

leaving the white men behind. All hands ran back
toward the ship, which was so fast in the sand that
she could not be freed quickly. La Salle ordered
that the men be rescued first, but it was growing
dark by the time that task was finished.

"Let the ship alone till tomorrow," he ordered.
"We will finish the work then."

During the night the wind grew high and the
waves rose, preventing rescue work the next day.
The ship, which some thought had been grounded
on purpose by those who did not like La Salle, split
to pieces from the force of the waves. Some pow-
der, meal, and blankets were saved; about thirty
casks of wine and brandy were washed ashore.

Most of the timber of which the ship had been built also floated to land.

Otherwise, all was a total loss. Indians stood around watching, and some of them stole a number of the blankets, which their squaws cut up and made into dresses. Although a raiding party of whites recovered some of them, the French seized several Indian canoes as punishment. The Indians replied by shooting arrows at them, killing two Frenchmen. La Salle certainly was having his share of trouble. He had lost two ships, both loaded with needed supplies, and he had missed his destination.

As if this were not enough, Captain Beaujeu (bō zhĕ) grew more and more contrary, and he influenced others. At length he made up his mind to leave.

"You say that stream there is the Mississippi," he told La Salle. "I was to stay with you only till you reached it. Now I am going home."

La Salle probably was glad to be rid of the trouble-making captain, but Beaujeu also took with him about forty men and large stores of provisions. La Salle did beg the Captain for some of the cannon balls which were aboard the *Joly*. The Captain would not give them up; he sailed away leaving La Salle with eight cannon but nothing to shoot in them! Of the four ships he had started with, only one was left!

The group remaining with La Salle had already set up camp, using as much of the wreckage of the old ship as possible. They dug pits in which to store their supplies of perishable goods and scouted the country to find game and food.

It was now clear to La Salle that he had missed the mouth of the Mississippi. What he did not know was that he had missed it by five hundred miles.

Leaving most of the group under the command of Joutel (zhoō tĕl′), a dependable and faithful friend, La Salle and a few chosen men started out on a search. At the head of the bay now called Matagorda Bay, he found a river flowing in from the north. His hopes rose. Maybe this was the Mississippi! He sailed up the river, but presently it grew narrow, the water became clear, and the trees grew smaller. On each side stretched miles of prairie land, where thousands of odd-looking animals grazed. La Salle did not know that they were buffaloes, so he called them cows. The Spanish later named it Lavaca, or Cow River. It certainly was not the huge Mississippi.

When La Salle returned to camp, he found everything in disorder. Many of his men were discouraged; some were even rebellious. A few of them had even plotted to kill Joutel who, learning of the plan, prevented them from carrying it out. The men were quarreling among themselves and were asking angrily, "Why did you bring us to this wild place to die?"

La Salle saw that something had to be done.

The first location of the camp had been a poor one, so he ordered that it be moved. The lone ship, the *Belle*, was loaded with provisions, as was also a broad square log float they built. These slowly made their way to the place on the river that had been chosen for the new home.

There a fort was built. Erecting it was a slow, painful job. Some of the timber left from the wreck was dragged several miles by hand to the new site. No large trees grew closer than three miles. They had to be cut, squared, and dragged by hand to the place of building, since there were no carts or horses to carry or pull them. La Salle himself marked the trees and saw that they were

put in their proper places.

At last the hard work was finished. The fortress was in the form of a square with a tall fence, or palisade, around it. At each of the corners was a tower containing a cannon, and in the walls were holes through which guns could be fired. New cannon balls were made with metal at hand. The building itself was large and divided into a number of small rooms. Underneath was a cellar, where ammunition and supplies were stored. Inside the palisade was a small chapel, where religious services could be conducted.

When the building was finished, the people were called together, and one of the priests spoke to them. Religious services were held, the flag of France was raised, and the place was solemnly named "Fort Saint Louis" in honor of the King. There were cheers and perhaps a few tears in the eyes of some who were present.

But La Salle had not yet discovered the river where he planned to found a colony, so he selected a small group of men and started on another search. There followed weeks of wandering among forests and swamps, sometimes without water, food, or sufficient clothes. Finally the weary men turned back toward the fort.

Conditions could hardly have been worse. The last ship, the *Belle*, had been lost in the nearby bay. The ammunition was almost gone. The Indians were becoming more hostile. Several of the colonists had died, and others, including La Salle, were sick.

Most men would have given up in despair, but La Salle refused to quit. The loss of the last ship made it impossible for the group to go home. Their only hope of rescue lay in finding the Mississippi and going up the river to Canada.

He made two or three other efforts, always taking along some of the men and leaving others to guard the women and children left at the fort. On one trip he went as far as the Trinity River, where he fell sick, probably with malaria. Some friendly Tejas Indians nursed him back to health and gave him a horse to ride as he returned to the fort.

As the party neared the fort, they heard sounds of music and laughter. It was a wedding party, said to be the first white wedding in Texas. Joutel had encouraged the marriage and celebration to take the minds of the colonists from their troubles.

La Salle took part in the celebration himself, but his mind was still on the Mississippi and Canada. He spent Christmas in the fort, but by the middle of January, 1687, he was ready for a final effort. This time he took his priest brother, his nephew Moranget, and Joutel. Also included were two who proved to be enemies, Duhaut and Liotot.

They followed a northerly course, crossing the

Colorado River probably near present Columbus or Alleyton. Winter rains fell, and they had much trouble crossing swollen rivers. La Salle sent eight men to fetch some corn which he had hidden on an earlier trip. They found it, damp and ruined, so the men had to depend largely on buffalo meat for food.

Then a long-brewing quarrel broke out between La Salle's nephew on one side and Duhaut and Liotot on the other. These two men killed Moranget one night. When La Salle, growing uneasy at the delay of the eight men, set out to find them, the same two killed him.

Then the party went to pieces. Some of the men returned to Fort St. Louis to build a ship and sail for France. Others, including Joutel, left the murderers on the pretense of trying again to find the Mississippi. Both Duhaut and Liotot were killed by another man who had quarrelled with them over the possessions of La Salle. A few, including Joutel, actually reached the Mississippi, and finally Montreal. From there they sailed for France, reaching their old home in October, 1688.

La Salle had failed to find the Mississippi or to establish a colony. The Spaniards, a few years later, found the ruins of Fort St. Louis. They uncovered chests which had been torn open and their contents scattered. Costly books were falling apart because of wind and water. A few guns were lying around, their stocks broken. In the ruins were three

skeletons. It was clear that the few Frenchmen who stayed in the fort had been killed by Indians. Searching parties found a few of the survivors among the Indians, but the full story has never been learned.

Even though La Salle had failed, his effort was important. He gave the French a basis for a claim to Texas that they did not give up until 1819. He scared the Spanish into establishing colonies in East Texas to outdo the French. Other Frenchmen later made settlements at the mouth of the Mississippi. La Salle was a forerunnner. What he had begun, others finished. He was one of the first white men to make a settlement in Texas.

— *J. A. Rickard*

Things to Do

1. Discuss the story, using these questions:
   a. Why did La Salle come to America in 1666?
   b. Why was he discontented with his new home on the St. Lawrence River?
   c. How did he finally reach the mouth of the Mississippi River?
   d. Why did he return to France after realizing his dream of finding "where the Mississippi emptied into the sea?"
   e. How did he convince Louis XIV that a settlement was necessary?
   f. Why did La Salle's ships miss the Mississippi River when they returned to make the settlement?
   g. Where did they land instead? Locate the spot on a map of Texas.
   h. What were some of La Salle's misfortunes in Texas?
   i. Describe Fort St. Louis.
   j. What became of La Salle and his followers?
   k. La Salle failed to build a colony for France on the Mississippi. What did he do instead?
2. La Salle was a trail blazer. Using outline maps of the World, the United States, and Texas, illustrate three of his voyages:
   a. The trip to the mouth of the Mississippi River.
   b. The second trip from France.
   c. His last attempt to find the Mississippi and Canada.
3. Use these maps and pictures to make an exhibit of La Salle's contribution to the exploration of America.

104

St. Denis in Texas

Before the end of the seventeenth century the French had made settlements in Louisiana. Far to the Southwest, in Mexico, and along the Rio Grande, the Spaniards had likewise made settlements. Though France and Spain were on friendly terms at that time, many believed the two nations would become rivals for control of Texas. At any rate, the French thought it wise to learn more about Spanish outposts. Accordingly, in 1714, Governor Cadillac of Louisiana, summoned St. Denis into his presence.

Luis de St. Denis (lōō′-ē dē săn-dē-nē′) made his way to the office of the Governor as soon as he entered Mobile (now in Alabama). An attendant ushered him at once into the presence of Governor Cadillac who, greeting his visitor cordially, explained, "I need a man to lead an expedition through Texas to Mexico," he began. "I understand you have had some experience of that kind."

"Yes, sir," replied St. Denis. "I was guide for a party that explored the Lower Mississippi, and I also helped explore the Red River."

"Excellent! You have been recommended by others with whom you have worked. Now here's our plan. You are to go to Natchitoches (Năck-ĭ-tŏsh),

and from there by land to Mexico. You may have
some capable men to go with you, and of course we
will bear all the expenses of the expedition, including proper pay for you and the men."

St. Denis accepted the proposal and at once
went to work organizing the expedition. He was
provided with a passport to the Spanish Governor,
so that he would be received as a friend. Into five
canoes he loaded provisions costing $2,000. A week
or more later he set out with twenty picked men.
After a brief stop at Biloxi, his home town, the

party moved on. Going with them were about thirty Indians. They went up the Mississippi River to its junction with the Red River, thence on that river to Natchitoches.

There they remained six weeks, while St. Denis assembled the Indians and gave them corn, grain, and farming tools and showed them how to use them. He even helped them build some log houses. Ten of the Frenchmen were left behind as guards, while the others started into Spanish territory. During the entire march they lived largely on food they killed while hunting. They met some Asanais Indians who were astonished to see them, never before having seen any French. St. Denis and his men smoked the pipe of peace with the Indians, after which they gave them presents and employed some of them as guides in search of the Spaniards.

In the village of the Asanais Indians was a woman named Angelica. She had been baptized by Spanish priests and spoke Spanish very well. As St. Denis also knew that language, he employed her as interpreter on the rest of the journey.

The expedition continued to live largely by hunting, as they moved slowly along, recording for future travel all rivers and their best crossings. Their route later became known as the Old San Antonio Road. At the end of six weeks they reached their first Spanish village, the Presidio del Norte, or the Mission San Juan Bautista, on the south bank of the Rio Grande.

One of his group, a man named Penicaut, later wrote an account of the expedition:

"As soon as we arrived," he wrote, "Don Ramon (Rä-mōń), a captain of the Spanish cavalry, came to speak with St. Denis, to learn the object of his visit. St. Denis told him that the Governor of Louisiana had sent him to open commercial relations with the Spaniards. The captain, who was a man of good sense, replied that he had no authority in the matter, but would write to the Governor of Coahuila (cō-ä-wḗ-lä) and give St. Denis an answer as soon as he should get orders from his superior. He then provided lodgings for the soldiers, and invited to his own house St. Denis, accompanied by his servant and myself!"

At length the Governor of Coahuila, who lived at Monclova, sent orders that St. Denis be brought before him. The French leader left his soldiers at the presidio, with orders to stay till he should return. A month later they were informed that St. Denis was going on to Mexico City, several hundred miles away. They returned to Natchitoches, but St. Denis did not return till the following year, 1715.

What caused him to stay in Mexico so long? This is a question difficult to answer. Evidently the Spaniards were suspicious of him. Travel was slow in those days. Then, there is a story that at the presidio there was a jealous lover who sent St. Denis to Mexico so he would be out of the way. The story goes on to say that he was imprisoned in Mexico

and would not have returned as soon as he did if his lady love had not gone into Mexico herself to rescue him.

One thing is certain: he had fallen in love with Manuela Sánchez (män-ōō-ā′-lä sän′-chāz), a granddaughter of the Spanish commandant at the presidio, and she returned his love. Before he left for Monclova, Mexico, they had become engaged. The journey was extended from Monclova, capital of the state of Coahuila, to Mexico City, capital of Mexico and home of its Spanish ruler, the Viceroy. The Mexican authorities questioned him closely, but they finally allowed him to return to the presidio on the Rio Grande.

There, in 1715, the two were married with much ceremony and feasting. Shortly afterward, the Viceroy of Mexico authorized St. Denis to go on an expedition into Texas, this time under the Spanish flag. Leaving his bride at the presidio, he aided in founding several Spanish missions in East Texas, returning to Mobile afterward.

But he was anxious to go back to the Rio Grande. Accordingly, he organized a trading expedition.

When he reached the presidio a second time, in April, 1717, he was not received so cordially. In fact, the Spanish officials seized the goods he had brought along for trading purposes and kept him in jail from June to late November on a charge of engaging in contraband trade. He was ordered to remain in Mexico City on bail, but he escaped and fled to the Louisiana city of Natchitoches. In time his wife joined him.

There he remained and for some years was a constant threat to the Spanish authorities. Perhaps the harsh treatment and imprisonment caused him to take this unfriendly attitude; perhaps he merely wanted to make a profit by trading. Certainly he engaged in trade with the Spanish when he could, and also with the Indians of the Red River and East Texas areas.

He lived out the rest of his life at Natchitoches, raising a family of five children and accumulating great wealth and property, including some Indian and Negro slaves.

His expeditions not only hastened the Spanish occupation of Texas, but also the development of the region. Among other accomplishments, he is credited with having laid out the *Camino Real,* or Old San Antonio Road. This gave the French an added reason to claim Texas. When the United States bought the French territory of Louisiana, she claimed Texas also; but, although many felt that she should not have done so, she gave up the claim in

1819. When Texas was finally admitted as a state in 1845, the work of St. Denis and others had borne fruit at last.

— J. A. Rickard

Things to Do

1. Using an outline map, trace St. Denis' journey into Texas. Illustrate the map with pictures of incidents that happened.
2. Use a "scale of miles" to determine the distance that St. Denis and his party traveled. How long did it take to make the trip? Compare this with the time required for the trip today.
3. Make a list of the Spanish words in the story, and find their meanings.
4. Are the East Texas missions still standing today?
5. What seemed to be the real purpose of the French in making an expedition through Texas?
6. Why was St. Denis chosen for the purpose?
7. How did a romance affect the course of Texas history?
8. Why did St. Denis go on to Mexico?
9. What aid did he offer to the Spanish?
10. Why was he later imprisoned and released?
11. Why is the St. Denis expedition important in the history of Texas?

Jean Lafitte

This is the true story of a famous pirate. Sometimes he was good; at other times he was bad. Maybe you can decide, when you read the story and *Things to Do*, why Lafitte was the kind of person that he seemed to be.

Jean Lafitte was born in Bordeaux, France, a port city near the Bay of Biscay. At a very early age he showed qualities of the celebrated freebooter which he later became. He ran away from home and enlisted for service on a British ship of war. He quickly tired of being a British sailor, deserted, and went to South America. About 1806 he became a privateer, sailed in and out of the West Indian seas, and in a few years he had acquired great wealth by his bold exploits.

Evidently Jean had an attractive personality; the men who worked with him were devoted followers and he made many loyal friends. From 1811 to 1813 the headquarters of Lafitte were on the island of Grand Terre, or Barrataria, about sixty miles from the delta of the Mississippi River. Lafitte had become a full-fledged pirate surrounded by a loyal band of followers.

In 1813 Governor Claiborne of Louisiana decided to break up the nest of pirates who plied up and down the coast. He offered a reward of five hundred dollars for the head of Lafitte. Swashbuckler that he was, Lafitte replied by offering fifteen thousand dollars for the head of the governor! Insulted and furious, the governor sent a military force to take Lafitte, who captured the governor's soldiers, loaded them with presents and sent them home again.

Governor Claiborne was more determined than ever to bring the bold pirate to justice. He sought help from the government of the United States. As a result, Commodore Patterson was dispatched with a fleet to break up the pirates' nest. The outlaws burned their town and retreated. Commodore Patterson gave up the fight, took his fleet and sailed away.

Between the years 1812 and 1815 the United States was at war with England. This gave Lafitte an opportunity long desired. He figured out a way to be pardoned by the United States government for the crimes he had committed as a pirate; he offered to fight in the war against England. The government believed that this would be an easy way to get rid of him. The bold rover fought gallantly behind the breastworks at New Orleans and was pardoned as he had so well planned.

The pirate spirit in Lafitte would not let him rest. Soon after the war he returned to his old habits and established himself on Galveston Island. He built a fort and a town which he called Campeche. Here, with perhaps a thousand followers,

he lived for years in royal splendor.

Doubtless because of his great personal charm, Lafitte had many chances to become a respected, law-abiding citizen. In 1819 he was appointed governor of Galveston Island by the Mexican Republicans. Again temptation overtook him. In 1820 an American schooner was taken by one of Lafitte's cruisers, plundered, and sunk. This was the signal for his ruin. In 1821 the United States government sent an expedition under Captain Kearney to take Lafitte. Again he tried the old tricks that had saved him before.

When the expedition arrived, the governor of Galveston Island went out to meet the captain, invited him and his officers to his house, and entertained them in a princely manner. The pirate, who was now a governor, was trying to make the captain and his men forget their real reason for coming to Galveston!

Captain Kearney failed to be turned aside by the flattery. He had come to take Lafitte and seemed determined to do it. Cunning Lafitte understood this immediately. He called his followers, paid them and bade them farewell. With a few chosen men and his favorite vessel, he abandoned Galveston forever. For years afterward he lived the life that he must have liked best—that of a hunted pirate who plundered Spanish ships. He died in Yucatan in 1826.

— Clyde Inez Martin

Things to Do

1. Make a list of the activities of Lafitte from 1806-1826. Your list could begin like this:
   1806—A privateer in the West Indian seas
   1811—Headquarters on the island of Grand Terre
2. Find other stories about Lafitte, the pirate. Compare them with this story.
3. Do you believe the following reasons given by Lafitte, according to Bancroft, the historian, were sufficient to justify his lawless acts?
Sailing homeward in his own vessel, he was cruelly attacked by a Spanish warship and robbed. Then, with his wife, he was put ashore on a desert island and left to starve. He was later taken to New Orleans by an American schooner, but his wife died from exposure.

Audubon in Texas

John J. Audubon, the famous naturalist, has given us many descriptions of plants and animals. However, there are few persons who know that he visited Texas in 1837, in the days of the Republic, and gave us an interesting description of President Sam Houston in the new capitol in Houston.

After wading through mud for whole days, exposed to scorching heat, and constantly annoyed by myriads of insects in the course of their numerous excursions on the shore, they [their party] reached Galveston Bay on the 24th of April. The fort of Galveston returned their salute of "26 fires," given by the big gun on the *Campbell,* and shortly afterward they received a visit from the Secretary of the Navy of the Republic of Texas, which under Sam Houston had declared its independence but a short time before their arrival. They were invited to proceed to the seat of government at Houston, eighty miles distant, in the interior.

They landed on the 26th of April, and after three weeks had been spent in exploring Galveston Island and its adjacent shores for birds and animals of all sorts, they started for Houston on the eighth

of May. After making about twelve miles their
vessel grounded on Red Fish Bar, and the party
then took to tender and gig, reaching their destination on the 15th. Wild turkeys, ibises, and ducks
of many kinds were seen in great numbers along
their course.

Audubon has left a graphic, a vivid account, of
what he saw at the capital of this short-lived infant
republic, including its picturesque president, the

melee of dejected [downhearted] prisoners then gathered there, and its Indians. Houston's abode was a small log house, "consisting of two rooms, with a passage through, after the Southern fashion."

"The moment we stepped over the threshold," said Audubon, "on the right hand of the passage, we found ourselves ushered into what in other countries would be called the ante-chamber. The ground floor, however, was muddy and unswept. A large fire was burning. A small table, covered with paper and writing materials, was in the centre. Camp beds, trunks, and different materials were strewn around the room. We were at once presented to several members of the Cabinet, some of whom bore the stamp of intellectual ability, simple, though bold, in their general appearance.

"The President was engaged in the opposite room on national business, and we could not see him for some time. Meanwhile, we amused ourselves by walking to the capitol, which was yet without a roof. And the floors, benches, and tables of both houses of Congress were as well saturated with water as our clothes had been in the morning.

"We first caught sight of President Houston as he walked from one of the shops where he had been. He was on his way to his house, and wore a large gray coarse hat. The bulk of his figure reminded me of the appearance of General Hopkins of Virginia for, like him, he was upwards of six feet high, and strong in proportion.

"But I observed a frown in the expression of his eyes that was forbidding and disagreeable. We reached his abode before him, but he soon came, and we were presented to His Excellency. He was dressed in a fancy velvet coat and trousers trimmed

with broad gold-lace. Around his neck was tied a cravat somewhat in the style of seventy-six.

"He received us kindly, was desirous of retaining [keeping] us for a while, and offered us every facility within his power. He at once removed us from the anteroom to his private chamber, which by the way was not much cleaner than the former. We were severally introduced by him to the different members of his cabinet and staff. Our talk was short; but the impression which was made on my mind at the time by himself, his officers, and his place of abode, can never be forgotten."

The party left Texas on the 18th of May.

— *Francis Herrick and John J. Audubon*

Things to Do

1. Discuss Audubon's visit to Texas by finding the answers to the following questions and reading them aloud from the story:
   a. How did Audubon come to Texas? Who greeted him on his arrival?
   b. Why did it take seven days for Audubon and his party to travel from Galveston to Houston?
   c. What were Audubon's impressions of Houston's cabinet members?
   d. Read his description of the capitol.
   e. What did Audubon think of President Houston?
2. Compare the kinds of wild life that Audubon saw on the Gulf Coast with that which can be seen today.
3. Are you a member of a Junior Audubon Club?

The Pig that Made History

If the treasury of the state of Texas had a mascot, it probably should be the carved figure of a pig, for it would remind Texans that a pig once kept the state from making an unnecessary debt.

This all goes back to 1841 when Texas was an independent nation. Her natural resources were undeveloped; her population small. Since the income was not enough to meet expenses, she was seeking a loan from France to make up part of the deficit. Prospects of securing the money were good. But there lived in the state capital of Austin a man named Bullock. He owned a pig that rooted its way out of the sty one day and strayed into the stable of M. de Saligny, French Minister to Texas. There the porker found some corn, feed intended for the minister's horse. The pig ate it!

Before the little thief had quite devoured the corn, de Saligny's servant caught him in the act and killed him. This made Bullock so furious that he horsewhipped the servant. Promptly the minister went to the sheriff who arrested Bullock but let him out on bail to await his trial.

Presumably, to talk over matters in a peaceable manner, M. de Saligny went to Bullock's home. However, he did not know the French minister's intentions. Without waiting for explanations, he ordered the Frenchman out of his house, using strong words to emphasize his command.

So far as de Saligny was concerned, this was "the last straw." He asked for his passports and returned to France.

A series of notes between Texas and France followed, and the affair almost reached the stage of an international crisis. The French regarded it as an insult and demanded a full apology. The Texans were not in the habit of apologizing about anything, but this time they saw the error of their way. The

Old French Embassy in Austin.

apology was finally made, but the loan was not granted. From the tone of the letters there is little doubt that the pig incident helped the French decide not to make it.

But the Texans concluded that things had happened for the best after all. They reasoned that if the loan had been made the state might have come under French influence, and then she might not have joined the Union. At the very least she would have made a debt that she did not need.

This dislike of debts has become a tradition with the Texas government. The "pay as you go" policy has long been popular in the state, and the Texas public debt is never allowed to go very high.

Maybe the Bullock pig deserves a monument after all.

— *J. A. Rickard*

Things to Do

1. Why was Texas asking France for aid in 1841?
2. What did the Bullock pig do to cause trouble between the two nations?
3. How was the matter finally settled?
4. What lesson have Texans drawn from the event?
5. Three things were done in this story by persons who were very angry. What were they?
6. What do you think would have been the outcome of the story if each of these persons had "cooled off" before acting?
7. How would the history of Texas probably have been changed?

French Villagers
on the Texas Frontier

Henri Castro probably was the most energetic of the empresarios or colonizers. He expended many years of his life and a large fortune on his dream of bringing colonists to settle on land granted him by the Republic of Texas in 1842. He brought to Texas a total of 5,200 desirable settlers. Although Castro was French, many of his colonists were German. His land was located in the counties of Medina, Uvalde, Frio, Atascosa, Bexar, McMullen, LaSalle, and Zavala. There were several village settlements in the colony, namely: Castroville, D'Hanis, Quihi, and Vandenburg.

August Santleben, the writer of the following story, was only five months old when his father and mother arrived at "Castro's Corner."

These colonists were transported across the ocean and conveyed to their destination at Castro's own expense, and he not only carried out his contract . . . with regard to the donation of land, but he added forty acres and a town lot to the allowance of each family. He assisted them out of his own means in every possible way until they were able to provide for themselves. He inspired his

126

own spirit into them, and encouraged them and others to occupy the desirable wilderness beyond until the western frontier was extended to the Nueces River.

A more attractive region did not rest under the dome of heaven, as I remember it, . . . Myriads of wild horses roamed the prairies at will, deer were everywhere and other game was abundant; the clear, running streams were full of fish, and quantities of honey in caves and hollow trees waited for those who cared to take it.

The first work my father did, after he became settled, was for Mr. Castro, who employed him and Mr. Huehner to dig a ditch on the west side of "Castro's Corner," for which he agreed to pay each of them fifty cents per day.

The ditch was eight feet wide and eight feet deep and it took them four months to complete the job. After the ditch was finished Castro leased a piece of land in the Corner to my father for three years, free of charge, except that he was to put it in cultivation.

My parents were affectionate and considerate in the treatment of their children and tried to raise them properly. They were also strictly religious, and they often tried to impress upon the minds of their offspring the importance of thinking and acting in accordance with the Ten Commandments so that they would not come in conflict with the law of their country.

My father was strongly impressed by the obligations and duties of his citizenship, and as he had come to the United States on account of its free institutions, he did not delay, after the expiration of five years, in taking out his naturalization [citizenship] papers which were secured in July, 1850.

My childhood years were passed happily and I had a good and easy time, although I helped my father all I could on the farm in light work or in making myself useful in many ways, but I never fancied farming very much . . . .

I remember a donkey which was identified with my school experiences that, incidentally, was the cause of many fights and any amount of trouble, but it is not worth while to discuss them. He had a disposition that was rather eccentric or contrary and he indulged his whims or fancies whenever it suited him. He was always in request on week days, and on Sundays some one of the children rode him to church. I will never forget the sensation he created one Sabbath morning when the services were being conducted. The minister was reading from the Bible and the congregation was devoutly listening to the lesson in which the word Hallelujah[1] appears. As he raised his voice to an unusually loud pitch when repeating the word, the donkey, that was grazing near the window, thought perhaps that the exclamation invited a response. A moment later his head appeared in the opening and he uttered a

[1]Praise or thanksgiving

refrain in prolonged notes such as only a donkey can express, until the solemnities were disturbed, and the preacher even, although somewhat confused, could not keep back a smile.

My father hired Paul Offinger to help him on the farm and he worked for him three years, in which time he saved up enough money to buy fifty acres of land near Quihi, eleven miles west of Castroville. When he moved on his place he had no one to assist him and my father hired me to him to drive his oxen when plowing or hauling for $5.00 per month and my board. I remained with him four months, and . . . . my duties were performed to the satisfaction of my employer.

In those days oxen were the only animals that were used on farms on the western frontier for draft purposes, partly because the original outlay and cost of keeping them was less than for horses, and another reason was the risk of losing them on account of Indians who were always stealing horses. The oxen were always yoked together, and after a day's work the yoke was removed, a bell was suspended to one of their necks, and they were turned out on the range until wanted, when the tinkling bell indicated their whereabouts.

Generally, I found it dull business wandering through the mesquite bushes in search of my oxen, but one foggy morning I had an exciting experience when I saw a panther in my path, feasting on a calf he had killed. He was only a few feet in front of me, but he was so intent on satisfying his hunger that he only looked at me without rising. I, on the contrary, was very much startled, but a spell of fascination crept over me which kept my eyes fixed on him as I slowly backed from his presence a few steps before turning, and then I ran towards home at the top of my speed. I was bare-footed, as was usual with country boys in those days, who only wore shoes on Sundays, and my toes clawed the ground and helped me along. I was making pretty good time when I stepped on a large rattlesnake that was coiled in my path, which filled me with

horror, but before he could strike I made a frantic
leap in the air and landed beyond his reach. The
accident lessened my fear of the panther and I reduced my gait to a walk. But these adventures did
not make me abandon my search, which I continued,
though with greater caution, until the musical ox-
bell in the distance guided me to the animals I was
seeking and I drove them home.

On another occasion Mr. Offinger went out
hunting one Sabbath morning, and he allowed me
to accompany him. He carried an old-fashioned
army musket, which was loaded with the only charge
of buckshot that he had, and I was unarmed. On
the east side of Quihi prairie we suddenly found

ourselves in the midst of a herd of about twenty-
five javelinas, or Mexican hogs, that were feeding in
a thicket of scrubby live-oak. When they saw us,
all of them bunched together with their heads

toward us while their teeth clashed in a threatening
and vicious manner until Mr. Offinger fired into
the bunch. As the gun fired they rushed towards

him and they moved so quickly that he only had time to climb a small tree beyond their reach. I was standing about twenty steps behind him and knowing the danger I followed his example, but as Mr. Offinger was the aggressor he received all of their attention. He wanted me to descend from my sheltered position and gather rocks with which to drive them away, but I was afraid, consequently we remained in our place of refuge until they disappeared an hour later.

The Mexican or musk hog, which is common in many sections of west Texas, has a sack on its back that contains a secretion which has a strong odor. They are aggressive, often attacking persons without being provoked, and when wounded they are dangerous. Their long, sharp tusks cut like a knife and it is difficult to avoid them when on foot because of their quick movements and manner of fighting.

During the time I served Mr. Offinger I had many hours of recreation and my tasks were never heavy. My personal expenses amounted to only twenty-five cents a month, that went for candy which I bought at Mr. Bailey's store in Quihi, and frequently my friend and playmate, Frank Rieden, now living in San Antonio, helped me to eat it. My wages were well earned, and when I received the nineteen dollars that was due me I returned home with the money and placed it in my father's hand with a great deal of pleasure. . . .

My father once contracted with a party in San Antonio to haul a load of pine lumber from a mill near Bastrop, on the Colorado River, and I went with him. Bastrop was then a small village with a few scattering houses, and the night we camped in the town a public meeting was held in the open air which I attended. I have no recollection of what it was about, although it was the first political speech I had ever heard, but I do remember that the place was lit up by torches made of pine-knots and that they furnished the most beautiful light I had ever seen. I was only about eight years old then, and when I learned that I could get pine-knots for the trouble of gathering them, I lost no time the next day in collecting all I wanted, although the task was not as easy as I expected. On the way home I illuminated our camp every night and had some left with which I lit up the premises, my home, to please a few of my friends. They were delighted, because they had never seen anything so brilliant before, but the exhibition closed when I barely missed setting fire to the corn-crib.

The light they had been accustomed to see was made by wrapping a rag around a stick and saturating it with lard; the lower end was then stuck in a coffee-cup half full of sand, and the cup was filled with rendered lard or melted tallow. It made a very dim light, but it was the best we could do before candle molds were introduced, which were used by everybody who made tallow candles, until sperm candles of northern manufacture were placed on the market. The first I ever saw was in Castroville, in 1855, when three of them sold for twenty-five cents; but they were too high-priced for common use and more than the poorer people of that region could afford to pay.

— *August Santleben*

Things to Do

1. What is an empresario?
2. Who was Henri Castro?
3. How did he obtain a land grant in Texas?
4. Where was his grant of land? Locate it on a map of Texas. Read the description of it from the story.
5. Can you list some of the personal qualities that were necessary to live on the frontier?
6. What caused merriment at church?
7. What did August earn when working for Mr. Offinger?
8. What caused August to run toward home, then suddenly stop?
9. Why did August have to climb a tree?
10. Where did August get his pine knots for lighting?

The People They Found

The Mexican Eagle

It is well-known that the eagle is the bird of honor for Mexico, as well as for the United States. The story of why it was selected by the Mexican nation is not so well-known.

It is a story about the Aztec Indians. Many centuries ago, in the time of the Middle Ages of European history, these Indians were wanderers far to the north of modern Mexico. Where they came from is not certain, but slowly they moved south, seeking a new home.

Finally, they reached a beautiful lake nestling in a high valley on a plateau. The valley, called Anahuac (än a´wäk), was perhaps sixty miles wide and a hundred miles long; and the lake, known as Texcoco, was in the valley's most pleasant part.

Other groups of Indians were there when the Aztecs entered the valley; in fact, they were the seventh group to enter. Perhaps the Aztec pilgrimage had lasted for centuries. Certainly they had lived for long periods of time in several places. In some of these places they had built homes, reared families, and raised crops.

Their priests, or religious leaders, declared that their gods wanted them all to migrate to a new land. In the land that was to be their new home would be a lake. In that lake would be a large rock, and on that rock a cactus would be growing. An eagle would be sitting in the cactus, holding in his claws a writhing snake.

This was the sign for which the wanderers kept watch as they slowly moved forward, enduring many hardships. Once they were enslaved by a more powerful race; but even after their enslavement they proved so fierce that their captors finally let them go free.

One morning, says the legend, a group of Aztec scouts came back to the main camp. They were in a great hurry to see their chiefs and priests, and as they ran, they told their news. They had found the promised land!

The priests and the chiefs followed the scouts to the place where they led. It was a high valley on the edge of a lake. There, perched on the stem of a prickly pear which grew from a crevice in a rock in the edge of the water, was an eagle of great size and beauty. His wide wings were opened to the morning sun as if he were ready to fly, but

strangely enough, he kept his perch. In his talons
was a live, writhing serpent.

Here was the sign for which the Aztecs long had
sought. They brought in enough earth to fill a part
of the lake and began to build their homes. It was
a long time before they became the rulers of the
valley, for other tribes were ahead of them. It was
a long time, also, before they built a large and beautiful city, but eventually they did. They called it
Tenochtitlan (Tā nōch tē tlän´) but after the coming
of the Spaniards its name was changed to Mexico
City. When the Spanish conqueror, Cortés, entered
Mexico, the city was ruled by a mighty chieftain, or

emperor, called the Montezuma. Today the city is the capital of Mexico. The lake is completely filled in and has disappeared, but some of the buildings of the city are gradually sinking, and cracks are appearing in their foundations. Architects say that is occurring because of the lake bottom on which the city is built.

But the growth of Mexico City continues, and the emblem of the eagle with the serpent is the national emblem of the Mexican nation.

— *J. A. Rickard*

Things to Do

1. Discuss the story, using the following questions:
   a. Where did the Aztecs live before reaching their final home?
   b. Why were they going on a long pilgrimage?
   c. How do you know that they stayed for several years in some places before moving?
   d. How did they know when they had reached the place that the gods chose for them?
   e. Why is the eagle a bird of honor in Mexico?
   f. What evidence is there that Mexico City was built upon a lake that had been filled in?
2. Make an illustration of the sign for which the Aztecs looked constantly as they wandered from place to place.
3. Ask your librarian to help you find information about the Aztecs to share with your class.
4. Would you like to write a legend about the founding of your own city? Are there facts about its location to give you ideas?

Advice of an Aztec Mother
to Her Daughter

The Aztecs were Indians who lived in Mexico many hundreds of years ago, before the Spaniards entered the country and conquered it. Many of the people of Mexico today are of Aztec blood. A Spaniard named Bernardino de Sahagun copied down the advice of this mother to her daughter. It is surprisingly modern.

Take care that your garments are decent and proper, and observe that you do not adorn yourself with much finery, since this is a mark of vanity and folly. As little becoming is it that your dress should be dirty or ragged; since rags are a mark of the low, and of those who are held in contempt. Let your clothes be becoming and neat, that you may appear neither fantastic nor mean.

When you speak do not hurry your words from uneasiness, but speak deliberately and calmly. Do not raise your voice very high, nor speak very low, but in a moderate tone. Neither mince when you speak nor when you salute, nor speak through your nose; but let your words be proper, of a good sound, and your voice gentle. Do not hesitate in the choice of your words.

In walking, my daughter, see that you behave

becomingly, neither going with haste, nor too slowly; since it is an evidence of being puffed up to walk too slowly, and walking hastily causes a vicious habit of restlessness and instability. Therefore,

neither walk very fast nor very slow; yet when it shall be necessary to go with haste, do so. In this use your discretion.

When you are on the street, do not carry your head much inclined or your body bent; nor should you go with your head very much raised, since it is a mark of ill breeding. Walk erect and with your head slightly inclined. Do not cover your mouth or your face from shame, nor go looking like a near-sighted person, nor, on your way, make fantastic movements with your feet. Walk through the street quietly, and with propriety.

Another thing you must attend to, my daughter, is that, when you are on the street, you do not go looking hither and thither, nor turning your head to look at this and that. Walk neither looking at the skies, nor on the ground. Do not look upon those whom you meet with the eyes of an offended person, nor have the appearance of being uneasy; but of one who looks upon all with a calm countenance. Doing this, you will give no one occasion of being offended with you.

Show a becoming countenance; that you may appear neither morose, nor, on the other hand, too obliging. See, my daughter, that you give yourself no concern about the words that you may hear in going through the street, and pay no regard to them. Let those who come and go say what they will. Take care that you neither answer nor speak, but act as if you neither heard nor understood them. If you act in this manner, no one will be able to say that you have said anything amiss.

Here in this world we travel by a very narrow,

steep, and dangerous road, which is as a lofty mountain ridge, on whose top passes a narrow path. On either side is a great gulf without bottom, and if you leave that path, you will fall into it. There is need, therefore, of much caution in following the road.

— *J. A. Rickard*

Things to Do

1. These questions are for girls to answer. The Aztec mother was trying to help her daughter grow into the kind of woman who would be respected in the tribe. Read aloud each thing that the mother told her daughter. Compare it with things that are expected of girls today in our culture.
2. Has your mother ever said some of the same things to you?

The Indians of Texas in 1836

Mrs. Holley, the author of this story, was a cousin of Stephen F. Austin. She lived in Texas when the Indians were here, and wrote a book about them. This story is a part of her book.

The Comanches inhabit the country to the north and northwest of San Antonio de Bexar. They do not cultivate the earth for corn, but depend altogether on the chase for a living. They have, however, villages located generally with native taste in some luxuriant and beautiful place that is easily protected, where they leave their women and children in their hunting and warlike excursions . . .

They follow the immense herds of buffalo which graze the vast plains of this region, often to the amount of thousands in one herd. These plains are also stocked with wild horses, which run together in droves of many hundreds. These horses are called, in the language of the country, mustangs . . . are not natives, but are descended from the stock brought over by the first Spaniards . . . . The Comanches catch and tame these wild horses, and when unsuccessful in the chase, eat them.

These Indians always move on horseback. Besides the bows and arrows, the usual arms of the Indian warrior, they are armed with a long spear,

having a sword blade for the point. A war party
of these mounted Indians is sufficiently frightening.
They are headed by two squaws, who by their
shrill voices, serve as trumpeters, and have various
tones to denote the different movements. When
they discover an object of attack or pursuit, they
dart forward in a column like lightning towards it.
At a suitable distance from their prey, they divide
into two squadrons or columns, one-half taking to
the right and the other to the left, and thus sur-
round it.

* * * The Comanches have one head chief
and many lesser ones. They hold regular councils

quarterly, and a grand council of the whole tribe once a year. At these councils all important matters are decided, and all prisoners taken for offenses are tried. Their discipline is rigid. If a hunting party takes the life of a North American after making him prisoner, without bringing him before the council for trial, the offenders are punished with death.

Not so with the Mexicans, who are considered as enemies and treated as such. The hatred is mutual, and is fully returned on the part of the Mexicans. Hence the origin of the epithet or word expressing loathing, so general in Mexico: to denote the greatest degree of hatred, they call a person a *Comanche*.

* * * The Carancahuas inhabited formerly the whole of the sea coast. They were said to be cannibals and very ferocious. Hence, probably, the Spaniards were little disposed to invade them, or to visit them without a strong military escort. Hence, also, it is less surprising that they learned very little about the coast, and thus they supplied in place of knowledge, tales of fictitious horrors.

The first settlers in this part of the country, under General Austin, arrived in considerable force and were well armed. The Carancahuas were sufficiently peaceable so long as the settlers remained in a body, annoying them only by begging and stealing whatever fell in their way. But when the settlers separated to explore the country to find a

suitable location, four of the number who were left
with the provisions and baggage to protect them,
were killed by these Indians, and their goods carried
off.

Then fighting commenced. The colonists were
not strong enough to give the punishment the Indians deserved. When the number of the colonists,
at last, was being much increased, they mustered
a party of sixty riflemen . . . General Austin commanded this expedition in person. The result was
the slaughter of half the tribe. The remainder took
refuge in the church of the Mexican Mission at La
Bahia. The priests were ordered to turn them

out . . . But after much persuasion a truce was granted them, that they should never again cross the Lavaca River, the western boundary of the colony. This engagement they have faithfully kept.

Recently, the Mexicans have commenced killing the remnant of this tribe, for some robberies and murders committed by them. The survivors have crossed the Lavaca, to the number of forty or fifty, to beg the protection of the colonists, offering to perform any kind of service or labor, in return for protection and food. The people on the frontier have, accordingly, distributed them amongst their families, as servants.

* * * There are remnants of several other tribes of Indians, the Wacos, Tehuacanes, Tonkawas, Lipans, &c., . . . but of too little note to merit particular notice. They are either too few in number to be formidable or important, or so far civilized as to provide well for themselves without disturbing others.

The Coushattas are most worthy of notice. They have their villages on the Trinity River, their houses are well constructed, and their fields well cultivated. They have good horses and cattle, use cooking vessels, and are hospitable to strangers. In autumn, when their crops are laid by, they range the country in small parties, to procure their winter's stock of venison and bear's meat, leaving their villages often without a single individual to protect them. They are few in number and quite friendly.

When among the settlements, they conduct themselves properly, and know the difference between a wild hog and one that has a mark on his ear.

The Kickapoos, Shawnees, Cherokees, and Creeks, driven by the people of the United States to the west of the Mississippi, sometimes extend their hunting parties to the settlements on the Brazos. They appear to regard the American settlers in Texas as a part of the people of the United States, and conduct themselves in a friendly and respectful manner.

— *Mary Austin Holley*

Things to Do

1. Make a list of the Indian tribes that are mentioned in the story. One person, or a small committee from your class, may find information about each of these tribes in other books about Indians.
2. Prepare a short program about the Indians of Texas, and share it with another class in your school.
3. On an outline map of Texas, locate the places where the Indian tribes lived.

Life Among the Comanche Indians

Have you ever wished that you could have lived—for a day or two, maybe—among the Indians? The writer of this story did live among the Comanches for a short time in the early days of Texas. When he was ninety-one years old he wrote about his experiences with the Indians. He learned many things about the Comanches.

The family meals, consisting of meat alone, generally roasted on sticks, were all served together on the flesh side of a dried skin, each fellow helping himself. Their drinking vessels were made of buffalo horns and terrapin shells, and some had even become possessed of a tin cup.

The vessels for carrying water were made of deer skins "cased"—stripped off whole—the legs and necks tied up tightly with sinews. Sometimes the smaller stomach pouch of a buffalo was used.

* * * They had some kind of a religious belief which seemed similar to sun worship. Judging from outward displays there was some power which it was necessary to please by offerings. When out on a hunt as soon as game was killed they struck fire and roasted meat, and always before eating a bite the chief would cut off a morsel and bury it; the first fruit of the chase, I suppose.

A similar ceremony was observed when the chief lit his pipe; the first puff of smoke was blown toward the sun and the second to the earth after the manner of incense offering; the substance used for the purpose was a mixture of tobacco and dried sumach leaves. The pipes were made of stone generally, though sometimes hard wood was substituted.

They evidently believed in a hereafter, but whether the conditions thereof depended on their conduct in this life was uncertain. One thing I know: though they would fight desperately to rescue the body of a fallen comrade so long as his scalp was intact, the moment he lost it he was abandoned. They would not touch the body even to bury it. . . .Another point on which they seemed to be superstitious was in never touching the heart of an animal. They would strip off every particle of flesh, leaving the skeleton entire and the heart untouched inside.

Although it was customary for the first fellow who woke in the morning to announce the fact in song, the act seemed rather a sudden free expression akin to that of the feathered songsters than a religious rite; the song itself was wordless save for the syllables, ha ah ha, . . . the performance ending in a keen yell.

* * * In cases of dispute, the council of the old men decided it, and from their decision there was no appeal. And when one died, all his belongings were destroyed, thus preventing any possibility of a family quarrel over his estate.

During the whole period of my sojourn among the tribe—three months—I did not hear a single angry dispute among the adult members. The youngsters had an occasional quarrel, which they were allowed to fight out, to the amusement of the onlookers.

. . . I never saw a woman or a child abused. The women, as in all savage tribes, were treated as slaves, but their inferiority, their low position, was their protection from punishment. . . .

An Indian brave would have felt it a burning disgrace to strike a woman. I don't think they ever resorted to bodily punishment within the tribe. . . .

There was a distinct line dividing the provinces of men and of women, the mother having complete control of the children. When an Indian girl arrived at a marriageable age, it was the mother who arranged the match; the suitor generally winning her favor by gifts, or barter of skins, and sometimes horses, if the girl was a belle.

The women, of course, performed all the labor, aside from killing and bringing in the game, stripping the skins from the animals, dressing and ornamenting them with beads or paint, ... The skins were first staked down to the ground, flesh side up. With a sharp bone the squaw then scraped off every particle of flesh; next the scraped surface was spread with lime to absorb the grease, after which the surface was spread with the brains of the animal, rubbing it in and working it over till the skin became soft and limber, the process requiring days and days of hard work.

Then with paint, which they manufactured from colored chalks, and brushes made of clusters of hair, the artist, with the earth for an easel, beginning in the center, drew symbolic designs, which she executed with a skill truly remarkable.

A multitude of different colored rays [from] a common center radiated out in finely drawn lines . . .

These painted robes were worn over the shoulders like shawls, the fur side underneath.

The old people of both sexes were treated with respect, . . . Little notice was taken of the female children by either parent, all their pride and affection being centered on the young warriors, fitting them out with bows and lances, with which they fought imaginary foes. . . .

The little Indian girls, . . . , played at dressing skins, setting up lodges, etc. Yes, and they played with dolls, too. I never was allowed to inspect those Indian doll babies, so I can't tell how they were made; but the little Indian maids bound them on pieces of bark, setting them up against trees, swinging them in hammocks or carrying them on their backs just as their mothers had done with them.

The small boys went entirely nude, but the girls always wore some covering. When not hunting, the bucks whiled away the time in telling marvelous stories of the fight and chase—the former for my benefit, I presume—running races, sometimes on horseback, sometimes on foot. I sometimes ran with them, and in a 50-yard dash could beat most of them, that distance only serving to limber them up. They always insisted on running at least a quarter of a mile, in which case they would outdistance me, so I declined to run over my limit. * * *

Occasionally they had visitors from other tribes with whom they swapped lies, sometimes conversing entirely by signs, not seeming to understand each other's language at all, though it all sounded the same to me. * * *

I often accompanied the bucks on their hunts, and rarely saw an animal killed in reckless sport, old buffalo bulls then being the victims. . . .

Another one of their sports . . . was the las-

soing of turkeys, deer, mustangs, and buffalo calves.

When a drove of turkeys ranged out on the prairie in pursuit of grasshoppers, the Indian would follow at a distance until the birds were a mile or so from timber; then he would dash upon them, causing them to rise. Putting spurs to his horse he would then keep right under the flock, keeping them on the wing until they fell to the ground from exhaustion, then he ran among them and lassoed all he wanted.

When he wanted venison, the Indian secreted himself near a watering place till the deer came in to drink, after which they became stupid and any good mustang could run upon them with ease. The

same tactics were pursued in the capture of mustangs, which often fed away ten or twelve miles from water, remaining until thirsty. By that time they were tired and sluggish, and they drank so much water that they could not move rapidly, thus falling an easy prey to the Indian's lasso. If veal or young meat was his desire, the Indian would start a band of buffalo, crowding them so closely that the calves could not keep up and, falling behind, were cut off and lassoed.

One of the Indian's principal grievances against the white man was the wholesale slaughter of the buffalo, which the Indians claimed were their cattle, placed there for them by the Great Spirit. White men would run upon a band of buffalo and shoot them down in careless sport, sometimes not even taking the hides. . . .

The country the Indians considered theirs by right of inheritance. They had learned the import [meaning] of surveying and never lost a chance to display their hostility toward it.

— *Noah Smithwick*

Things to Do

1. Write six fact questions about the Comanche Indians that are answered in the story. Ask these questions of classmates. The following questions are suggestive of ones you may make:
   a. Why did the writer think that the Comanches were a religious tribe?
   b. How were women and girls treated?
   c. What sports were enjoyed by boys?
2. In what ways were the Comanches like other Indians about whom you have read?
3. Why are the Comanches of interest to Texans?

Indians in Texas Today

Do you know that there is an Indian reservation in Texas? Near the "Big Thicket" in Polk County, Texas, lives a small remnant of two tribes of closely related Indians. They are wards of the state of Texas. They were given a part of the land on which they live as a reward for their long record of loyalty.

They are all that is left of a tribe with which De Soto met in 1541. Afterward, they were lost to view until they showed up in the French-owned

Gulf region, on a tributary of the Alabama River. At first they warred against the French but later became friendly to them and settled in Southern Louisiana.

When the United States bought Louisiana, trouble arose between whites and Indians. Some of them moved to Texas in the early nineteenth century. The Alabamas settled on the west bank of the Neches River and the Coushattas on the east bank of the Trinity, both near the Gulf.

They were neutral during the War of Texas Independence. Because of good behavior, they earned the respect of President Lamar who strongly distrusted Indians. He proceeded against other Indians in Texas, but these Indians were left in peace on their lands.

After Texas joined the Union in 1845, the state kept up the wardship of these Indians, although the federal government took charge of other tribes in the state. An Indian reservation was set aside in the Upper Brazos region for all the Indians of the state. In 1858 Congress passed a law setting aside $5,000.00 to pay the expenses of moving the Alabamas and Coushattas, if they would give their consent.

The Indians refused to give consent. Four years earlier, after the Indian reservation had been established in the Upper Brazos region, they had settled the matter, so far as they were concerned.

At that time, or a little earlier, a meeting was

held at the home of Samuel Rowe, of Polk County, and there, through interpreters, the Indians made known their grievances. They had been robbed of land by whites and two or three times had been forced to move. They had been accused of stealing and other crimes of which they were not guilty. They wanted the state to give them two sections, 1280 acres, of land in that region, where they wished to live and die.

Their pleas must have been forceful, for forty-two white men present signed a petition asking the state to give the land to the Indians. The state legislature acted favorably. The land was purchased about seventeen miles from the town of Livingston, and 330 Indians settled there.

It was heavily timbered and hard to cultivate, but in a short time the Indians had some of it cleared and improved, and its crops belonged to all. Log cabin homes arose quickly, with real floors and chimneys and, sometimes, with little front porches. Patches of corn and potatoes appeared, fruit trees were planted, and cattle and horses grazed in nearby pastures. Several thousand hogs were grown for meat, and the neighboring thickets contained wild game.

Here the Indians, long homeless, had a home at last. They worked their own crops in season and hired out to white neighbors for extra spending money. Some white people had confidence in them, although some wanted to drive them away. But they resisted all efforts to move them, and they still call the place home today. Alabama or Coushatta Indians may wander to other places and even live there, but they still think of their East Texas home as their real one.

They were now contented, in a world of their own, where they could live their own lives. In the presence of whites they said little, but with each

other they were different. They were kind, warm-hearted and gay, hospitable and happy in their home life. They were fond of festivals, liked ball playing and other games, and enjoyed dancing. Also, they liked very much bright-colored clothing and silver ornaments. Sometimes their women put on flowered chintz skirts and the men wore bright shirts with feathers on their heads as they rode horses into town. Occasionally, silver pendants hung from Indian noses, and often large black umbrellas kept off sun and rain alike.

Most of the Indians were Alabamas, but a few Coushattas lived on or near the reservation. The two groups were of the same racial stock and inter-married freely. Their native languages were slightly different, but they could understand each other.

They had not been in their new home long when the four-year Civil War came. In many other places the Indians favored the Northern government, but the Alabamas and Coushattas were loyal to the government that their state favored. Some of them enlisted, and they formed a Home Defense company for service in Texas.

That was probably the reason why the Texas people kept them as wards afterward. Efforts were made to place them under the federal government, which had control of many other tribes, but they remained as wards of Texas.

They had been poor during the Civil War, but by 1880 they were again prosperous. Gradually they began to take on habits and practices of their white neighbors. The first step in this direction was in their adoption of white men's names. They began this practice as early as 1840, largely because of legal troubles over property ownership in court records.

With the coming of the missionaries, other white men's customs were adopted. Today their houses, farming methods, education, gardening, singing, reading of magazines, uses of medicine and doctors — all these show the influence of the whites.

However, certain Indian traits still persist, and one of them is their liking for group action. All personal differences and quarrels are settled by the group. Much of their work is done in the same way. They build homes, drill wells, cut the winter's supply of wood for church or school, and harvest their crops by common action.

Another outstanding trait is their religious devotion. Ninety per cent of the whole village of about three hundred people attend Sunday School and church regularly. Perhaps their common ownership of the reservation promotes common efforts. Not all their homes are on the reservation. A few years ago fourteen families lived near it; these were largely families who had intermarried with the Coushattas. The United States in 1928 added 3071 acres to the original 1280, the two tracts adjoining each other.

They are subject to state and county laws but

are not full-fledged voting citizens of Texas. The state has erected better buildings for them, has given the seeds for crops and livestock, and has provided medical services for them. A full-time agent looks after their needs. They have teachers to train them in agriculture, shopwork, domestic science, and the common school subjects.

They have earned this kind treatment. Throughout the years they have remained peaceful and friendly. Few crimes have been committed, and they respond well to efforts to educate them. Sometimes they produce the best writers, spellers, or singers at the county school meet, and their basketball teams are generally good. The girls of the domestic science class in their school furnish good school lunches for them.

In a few words, they are not only good citizens but also good Texans.

— *J. A. Rickard*

Things to Do

1. Locate, on a map of Texas, the Alabama and Coushatta Indian Reservation.
2. Most of the Indian reservations in the United States are owned by the federal government. Why is this one owned by the state of Texas?
3. Compare the Alabama and Coushatta Reservation with other reservations in the United States?
4. Visit the reservation, if possible, or try to find out more about these Indians by writing to Alabama and Coushatta Indian Reservation, Livingston, Texas.

Adventure in Early Texas

Ad. Lawrence's Ride

Many a thrilling incident of border life connected with the early history of Texas will never be recorded. It has been the lot of the writer to become acquainted with some of the early settlers of that State, and to hear them tell many a tale of danger and of daring. One of them is here narrated.

Adam, or Ad, Lawrence settled near the head waters of the Trinity River, in Texas, in 1829. . .

At the time the writer of this sketch first became acquainted with him, he was upward of sixty years of age, modest in manner, simple and unaffected in language. Rough as he appeared to the casual observer, he was kind and gentle, and the following incident as it fell from his lips, bore the impress of being a simple recital of unvarnished facts. In the summer of 1832, Ad. Lawrence, with three other men, went out mustanging.

A brief account of the mode in which these hardy frontiersmen were wont to capture wild horses of the prairie, will interest the reader.

A few expert riders, mounted upon strong and fleet horses, and each provided with a strong rope, having discovered a herd of mustangs, would gradually approach to within a short distance of them, and then making a simultaneous dash among them, would each throw a lasso over the neck of one, and after a vigorous and exciting contest of half an hour or more would generally succeed in capturing their prizes. The mustangs, after being once conquered, are easily managed, and by kind treatment soon become perfectly gentle. Some of them are beautiful animals, "pretty as a picture," and most of them being natural pacers, make excellent riding horses.

These wild horses frequented the prairies of Texas at the time of my story. Even since the writer's advent to this State, in 1850, he has seen several large herds. Of late years, they have retreated before the approach of the white man, to more distant hills.

When about ten miles from the nearest settlement, and far out in the broad prairie, Lawrence and his companions discovered a herd of mustangs feeding, a mile or two distant. They approached them cautiously. As they came nearer, the horses, about one hundred in number, showed no signs of fear; and when noticing this singular circumstance, the long grass of the prairie suddenly became alive with Indians. The remainder of the story will sound better in Ad's own language.

"There was one to each pony, and they all mounted at a jump, and made for us at full speed, coiling their lariats as they rode. There was no time for swapping horses, so we all turned tail and made a straight shoot for the nearest settlement on Trinity, about ten miles off. Our animals were all fine, but the nag I was on was a bay mare a little ahead of any thing in that country for speed and bottom [endurance]. We rather left them the first three miles, but then their ponies began to show themselves. I tell you, you've no idea how much an Indian can get out of them mustangs. Instead of being a weight to them, they seem to help them along, and they kept up such a powerful yelling, 'pears like you might have heard them to Red River. We noticed that they divided, one-half striking off to the left, and we soon found out the reason, for we

quickly came to the bank of a deep gully or ravine, which had to be headed; it couldn't be crossed. They knew every inch of the ground, and one party made straight for the head of it, while the balance struck in below us to cut us off in that direction. 'Twas no use talking. We had to ride about a quarter of a mile to the left, right in their very faces, and head that branch. My nag was still tolerably fresh. The others were beginning to blow right smartly. I rode just fast enough to keep in the lead. I didn't care particularly about getting off without knowing what became of my companions. Just as I came to the head of the hollow, the Indians were within about one hundred yards, and yelling awfully.

"They thought they had us sure. I gave my mare the rein, and just touched her with my spur, and turned the corner with about fifty arrows whizzing about my ears. One stuck in my buckskin jacket, and one in my mare's neck; you may believe she didn't go any slower for that. For awhile I thought she cleared about twenty feet at a jump.

Soon as I got headed right again, I looked around to see what had become of the others. One look showed me. They were all down. About half the redskins had stopped to finish them, and the balance were coming for me like red-hot lightning. I felt kind of dizzy like for a minute, and then I straightened up and determined to get away if I could. I hadn't much fear, if I didn't have to head another branch. I could see the timber of the Trinity three miles away, and I gave my mare her own head. She had been powerful badly scared, and had been working too hard, and she was puffing a good deal.

"I managed to pull out the arrow which was sticking in her neck. Then I worked off my heavy buckskin coat, which was flopping about with the arrow sticking in it, catching a good deal of wind, and threw it away. I kept on about a mile further without gaining or losing much. Then I made up my mind to stop and let my nag blow a little, because I knew if I didn't she couldn't hold up much longer. So I pulled up, and alighted and looked around. Seemed as if the whole country was alive with them. About forty in a bunch a few hundred yards behind, and one not a hundred yards off. I loosened my saddle-girth so she could breathe good, took my bridle in my left hand, and pulled my butcher knife with my right. It was the only weapon I had, I had dropped my rifle when I got dizzy. The Indian was game. He never stopped until he got within ten feet of me. Then he throwed away his bow, jumped off, and came at me with a long knife like mine.

"There wasn't time for a long fight. I had made my calculations, and he was too sure he had me. He ran full against my knife, and I left him lying there. I heard an awful howl from the others, as I pulled off my heavy boots, tightened my girth, and mounted. A few minutes more and I struck the timber of the Trinity, and made the best of my way through it to the river.

"I knew that for miles up and down the banks were bluffs, and fifteen or twenty feet high. Where I struck the river they were about fifteen. I knew if my mare wouldn't take the leap I had to do it without her. She stopped an instant and snorted once or twice, but hearing the savages yell close behind, she took the jump. Down — down we went, full fifteen feet, plump into the deep water. We both went under for a second, then she rose, and struck out for the opposite bank with me on her back. Poor creature, she got about two-thirds across, and then gave out under me with a groan. I tell you I fairly loved that animal that moment, and I hated to leave her as bad as if she'd been human.

"I swam the rest of the way and crawled out on the bank pretty well used up. But I was safe. I saw the howling and disappointed savages come to the bank I had left, but not one of them dared take the leap. And the distance was too great for

them to shoot. So I rested awhile and then made
the best of my way to the settlements."

— D. W. C. Baker

Things to Do

1. Describe the manner of capturing wild horses.
2. Tell why the horses showed no signs of fear, as Ad. Lawrence and his friends approached.
3. Why did the Indians divide forces in the chase?
4. What made Ad. Lawrence's mare run faster?
5. What happened to Ad. Lawrence's friends?
6. Tell about the encounter of Ad. Lawrence with the Indian in the lead.
7. Describe the final leap of Ad. Lawrence's noble horse and his escape.

Escaping to the Music of a Violin

Carefully preserved in a glass case at the State Library in Austin is a crudely made, rough looking violin which bears the plain marks of age. It was made by Henry Journeay, one of the prisoners of the Mier (mē äŕ) expedition, while he was confined in Perote Castle, near Mexico City. What was more, the violin helped some of those prisoners to escape.

Journeay was a member of the volunteer Texas army that started out in pursuit of General Woll, who had led Mexican troops in the surprise seizure of San Antonio in 1842. His attack was so sudden that he captured a Texas court in session, including both judge and jury. These, with some other Texas citizens, the Mexicans took as prisoners as they fled back to Mexico.

Journeay and his companions set out to get revenge for the invasion, but at the town of Mier, on the Mexican side of the Rio Grande, they surrendered to a larger Mexican force.

Then began a long, weary march to Mexico City, but at Salado the prisoners overcame their guards and escaped. They were soon recaptured, and as punishment it was ordered that every tenth man should be shot.

The others were kept at hard labor for some time; then they were imprisoned in Perote Castle,

near Mexico City,. an old fort with thick stone walls.
Near the castle was a carpenter shop, and those
prisoners who were mechanics were put to work in
it. Journeay was one of these. Work was found in
the prison for the other prisoners.

In the shop Journeay found some pieces of well-
seasoned wood, which he smuggled into his cell.
With them he made a violin, using an old file and
a piece of broken glass for his tools. From some
place, we know not where, he secured violin strings.
In some way he obtained a long piece of tough wood

and some horse hair for a bow. Glue came from the shop.

For many nights he worked. Finally, his violin was ready to play. His Mexican guards may have thought it was a part of his shop work, or they may have liked the music. At any rate they offered no objections to his playing it in the large cell where many of the prisoners were kept. The other prisoners were delighted. As they listened to such tunes as "Buffalo Girl", "Molly Put the Kettle On", and "The Girl I Left Behind Me", they thought of home. At times they joined hands and danced in a circle, keeping step to the music. At other times they patted their feet, clapped their hands, or just sat and listened. Prison life, bad at best, became more endurable for them.

Then, one of them thought of a daring plan: dig a hole through the thick walls and escape! Those who worked in the shop managed to slip several chisels into the prison. With these they began to pick away at the walls.

It was a slow and dangerous task, for the walls were hard and thick, and if they were caught they would surely be punished. The rock broke into small pieces and into dust; both had to be removed to prevent the guards from seeing them. There was a window with openings large enough to poke a hand through. At night, when the wind was blowing, they threw out the chipped stones and the rock dust.

The chiseling made a noise, too, but here was where the violin helped. As Journeay played and the other men danced or patted their feet, the chisels were at work, and the two kept time with each other. The door to the cell was fastened with a large lock, which the guard could not open easily. If they heard him scraping at the lock, they quickly hid their chisels and covered up the chipped stones and rock dust.

It took many months of patient work and many tunes from Journeay's violin to make the hole, but finally through this tunnel many Texas prisoners escaped to liberty and home. Other Texans, including Journeay, who remained behind, later were released. At last, he too reached home, carrying his violin with him.

It remained in the family many years, but finally it was given a well-deserved place of honor in the state capitol.

— *J. A. Rickard*

Things to Do

1. Why did the Mexican army invade Texas in 1842?
2. Why did General Woll take back some Texans as prisoners?
3. What happened to the Texans who invaded Mexico?
4. How did Journeay manage to make his violin?
5. To what use was it put?
6. What finally became of it?

A Narrow Escape

Governor Sul Ross was captain of a Texas Ranger company in 1859 and 1860. This is a true story that was told by a member of his company. In the early days of Texas, the foes of the Rangers were Indians. Here, a lone Ranger narrowly escaped capture by a thousand Comanches!

Shifting the weight of his lean body from one stirrup to the other, and dropping the reins on his horse's neck, Frank Gholson again read the letter from his mother, which a fellow Ranger had brought from Fort Cobb.

Dated at Waco, July 7, 1860, it informed him of the recent death of his father and urged him to return at once to take charge of the farm and ranch.

Of course he would have to go, for he was the only man left in the family. That point was settled, so far as he was concerned; it only remained to obtain the captain's consent.

At any rate he had seen five months of stirring service since his enlistment at Waco in March; and here he was, in the Indian Territory, a Texas Ranger, along with a company of federal troops, looking for hostile Comanches.

They had been lucky since arriving at Fort Cobb, for Chief Plasedo and his friendly Cherokee followers had helped them chase the Comanches; but it had been a hard chase against a wily foe, and it was not yet over. One band of the enemy had crossed Red River into Texas, and another had turned north. Either force might return at any time.

But that was no longer his concern, since the courier sent to headquarters for the mail had brought him this letter.

He found Captain Ross in his tent and silently handed him the letter.

The captain read it and looked up. "I am sorry, Frank. I suppose you want a discharge so you can leave?"

"Yes sir, I hate to leave you, but I guess I have no choice, sir."

"Oh, there won't be any trouble about the discharge, but I'm afraid you'll never get there. You will have to travel through at least three hundred miles of hostile Indian territory before you reach a white settlement large enough to afford you any shelter at all. And the Comanches and Kiowas are in an ugly humor—a very ugly humor." The tall captain emphasized the last words as he shook his head regretfully.

"I know it, sir, but I'm afraid I must go anyhow," replied Frank, as he rose from the camp stool.

The captain also stood up. "The discharge will be ready for you in the morning; also your pay. I suppose you will be leaving then?"

Frank nodded and Captain Ross extended his hand. "Well, you are a good Ranger, Frank, but I don't need to tell you that you may soon need all your skill. If I should not be around when you leave, I now wish you good luck. Write me after you get home."

They shook hands warmly, and Frank left to make preparations for his long trip. He had already decided to travel as lightly as possible, but there were two things he had to have: firearms and something to eat. He oiled and loaded his pistol and carbine, secured plenty of ammunition, and filled one saddle pocket with bacon.

"This meat will keep me from having to hunt along the road, when I don't really have time to do it," he thought, as he loaded his saddle pockets, "and if I get in a tight place I can eat it raw."

Nearly all the Rangers in camp were on hand to see him off, and they gave advice freely.

"You'd better do most of your travelin' at night," suggested Ned Tompkins, veteran scout of the company. "Lay up in the afternoons, especially. This August afternoon sun will be hard on your horse."

"Keep a good watch for water holes and hiding places," advised another Ranger, "and keep the North Star straight behind you at night."

The friendly Indians were as interested in Frank's departure as were the Rangers. Chief Pla-sedo and Caddo Tom, with whom he had made friends, gave him more counsel.

"Comanche smart; be more smart," the two managed to tell him in broken English. "No much ride daytime. Heap ride night time. All time look, listen. Hear, see Comanche, go round. When sleep, keep one eye open. Maybe so Comanche no get you." Even while saying it, they shook their heads doubtfully.

"Oh, we'll make it all right, Pal and I," said Frank confidently, as he rubbed the hips of his fat four-year old horse. "There's not an Indian pony anywhere that this horse can't outrun."

Apparently the horse agreed with him, for he stuck out his black nose and nudged Frank's hand as he prepared to mount.

Frank had already decided on his daily course, provided the Comanches didn't interfere. He would ride due south, with the sun as a guide by day and the North Star to direct him by night. He would travel all morning and into the early afternoon, until he found water and a good place to hide. Then he would rest, graze his horse, sleep until midnight, and start out again. If he found signs of Indians, he might have to change his plans.

That program was followed four days, with no sign of Comanches anywhere. There were no roads to follow, but the country was largely open prairie.

Both the days and the nights were almost cloudless, and he had little trouble keeping his bearings.

But on the fifth day he began to see Indian signs. At one place he crossed the trail of a large herd of horses. From the crooked paths that most of the animals made, he judged that a loose herd was being driven by three riders.

Still later, he found a campfire that he judged could not have been more than two days old, and around this fire he counted many moccasin tracks. He began to be uneasy as he continued his southward course. He had so much trouble in finding a suitable camping place, with water and grass, that it was late afternoon before he stopped.

At last he came to a wooded creek, where he found a deep hole of water, fed by a spring. At sight of the welcome water, his tired horse broke into a trot, and Frank himself eagerly jumped down and knelt by the stream, for his canteen had been dry since three o'clock.

Pal put his mouth to the water, then snorted uneasily and backed away.

"Easy, old-timer," coaxed Frank soothingly as he tightened the reins. "Come on and get a drink."

When the horse pulled back and continued to show fear, Frank began to look around, and quickly learned what was the trouble. Floating in the water ten feet away was a bloody shirt. A crooked pole in Frank's hands soon revealed that the shirt was on the body of a white man, and with the pole Frank

dragged the body to the bank.

Who he was, Frank had no way of knowing, for there were no marks to identify him. But there could be no doubt as to what had happened. There was a deep, jagged arrow wound in his breast, and he had been scalped.

After scouting around awhile, Frank decided that the murderers were the same Indians whose trail he had already crossed.

"He probably was following them to recover livestock that had been stolen from him," was his comment as he finally returned to the body. "Well, I can't give the poor fellow much of a burial. It will have to be a watery one." So saying, he weighted the body with rocks and sank it in the hole.

"Now, let's get away from here, Pal," he said as he patted his horse's nose and threw the reins over his mane. "We do need rest but we'll have to take it somewhere else."

A mile farther up the creek he found a good place, with plenty of grass. There he stopped, staked his horse, and cooked supper.

"I'm almost afraid to sleep," he said to himself, "but since the redskins have already been along this way, maybe they won't come back. I must rest this horse, and I'll lie down near the stake. If anything goes wrong, he'll wake me with his snorting. I certainly can't stay in this country long, though: it's getting too dangerous."

The sun was still shining when he lay down. Before he did so, he put back on Pal the blanket and saddle that he had taken off when first he had stopped, but this time he fastened the girth loosely for Pal's comfort.

"We may have to get out of here sudden-like," he said to Pal. The faithful animal turned his head toward Frank, then stuck his nose back into the deep grass. The tired youth lost no time going to sleep.

It was dark when he awoke. Pulling up the stake and looping the rope as he went, he slowly made his way toward Pal. Tightening the girth, he swung into the saddle.

"Come on, Pal, we are still in the danger zone," he said as he crossed the creek and again turned south, with the North Star at his back.

Two hours he rode, and he had begun to feel that perhaps the danger was past, when he saw the twinkling of lights far to his right. More of them kept springing up until he counted thirty-two. Suddenly he saw straight in front of him a herd of noisy, stamping animals. He dismounted and looked at them in the darkness.

"Horses," he muttered, "and tame ones at that. And those lights must come from Comanche camp-fires. Why, there must be a whole army of them. Pal, we've got to change our course again."

He gently pulled the left rein and bore to the east, while the snorting, stamping, grazing horses continued undisturbed. It was an hour before he had finally made his way around them and again turned south.

For another hour he rode, but by that time Pal was showing signs of fatigue. When horse and rider went down off the flat prairie to a lower hilly region, Frank stopped and dismounted. Selecting a gully which was shut off by a hill on the north and by cottonwood trees on each side, Frank led his tired mount into the natural hiding place and pulled off the saddle and bridle, leaving only a halter and a rope on the horse.

"This is the safest place we'll find from the redskins," said Frank to Pal. "We've got to have some rest."

He fed Pal leaves from the cottonwood trees and watered him from a spring at the head of the gully. As for himself, he decided it was safer to eat his bacon raw. "The smell of fried bacon travels pretty far on the night air, and some prowling Co-manche might smell it and get suspicious," he thought as he whittled off a hunk of the raw bacon and began to chew on it.

He lost no time going to sleep, but an hour

later his nervous horse awoke him. He seized
Pal's nose, for in the light of a full moon he could
see a band of fifteen Indians driving a large herd
of horses off the prairie into the brakes below. Pal
tried to snort, as the Indians came nearer. Frank
was compelled to cut off the horse's wind until the
animal could hardly breathe, to keep him from attracting the enemy. When Frank felt safe, he took
a deep breath and removed his hands from Pal's
nose.

"Whew, but that was a close call!" he told his horse. "There must be at least a thousand of them. You've behaved like a gentleman, old boy, and when we get back to civilization I'll see that you have some of the best oats that can be found."

Frank was in no hurry to leave, for he wanted to be sure the Comanches were clear out of the country before he moved. It was almost sundown when he finally saddled up and rode south.

Three mornings later a tired horse and rider crossed the Red River into Texas. By late afternoon they stopped at a ranch house which marked the northern limits of white settlements. After resting and telling his tale to the friendly owner, Frank traveled by easy stages to home and friends.

Told by Frank Gholson to J. A. Rickard

Things to Do

1. What message did Frank receive?
2. What advice did his friends give him as he started home?
3. What Indian signs did he see?
4. In what danger did he find himself?
5. What did he do to keep his horse quiet?
6. Tell about the last days of his trip.

Maximilian's Gold

Somewhere near the Old Horsehead Crossing of the Pecos River in southwest Texas lies a fortune believed to be worth a million dollars. Wind and sand have erased all the old landmarks leading to it, but it is there all the same. At least this is the belief of many old-timers, and there seems to be enough proof to place the yarn out of the legend class and to give it a strong basis of possibility.

One spring morning, Bill Murdock and four other ex-Confederate soldiers found themselves seated in their saddles on the north bank of the Rio Grande, several hundred miles below El Paso. The men had recently served in the Confederate Army and were now greatly concerned about the Reconstruction period that followed the Civil War. Bill picked up the reins on his horse's withers and was about to enter the shallow waters of the river.

"There she lies, boys; land of fame and fortune," he was saying. "If we're going to get away from Carpetbaggers and Yankees, and maybe help Maximilian, here's our chance."

His horse had already taken the first step into the murky stream when one of his companions said, "Hold it! Somebody's coming. By the saints and Old Jeff, it's a wagon train!"

It was; there were ten heavily loaded wagons, drawn by mules, and carrying what the grizzled Austrian caravan leader declared to be cargoes of wool and hides. The Mexican drivers spoke no English, but the leader could talk with the ex-Confederates in their own tongue. And naturally the groups asked each other questions.

What the Austrian told Murdock and his men was not encouraging. The Emperor Maximilian, he said, was about to be overthrown. The Mexican Republicans under Juárez were rapidly gaining control of the country, and the Emperor's troops were deserting him. French troops, who had been supporting him and enabling him to rule, had been withdrawn from the country. The caravan had had trouble in getting out, and the Americans would be joining a lost cause. The caravan hoped to make its way across Texas to Galveston, where the cargo would be sold for money to take the Austrian back home.

Murdock, speaking for his men, told the caravan leader that their prospects for getting across Texas were far from bright. The Carpetbag government, then ruling the state, could not keep law and order, and the Indians were almost sure to attack them. They would never get through without guides and an armed escort.

As a result of this exchange of information, the caravan leader offered Murdock and his friends three hundred dollars each to escort them safely to their destination. Their offer was accepted. Within twenty-four hours, the Americans were taking the caravan back over the trail that they themselves had just traveled. They were San Antonio bound.

But they were not far up the road when Murdock's men grew suspicious. They doubted the word of the Austrian about the cargo. The wagons were too heavily loaded to contain wool and hides; they must contain something of greater value. And the actions of the drivers aroused their suspicions still more. Each wagon was fully covered with bows and sheets, and its contents were further covered, so that no one could see them. Moreover, the drivers stayed with them by day and slept in

them at night. A few efforts on the part of Murdock's men to peep met with a stern warning from the caravan leader.

One night the guides held a caucus on the matter. Some of them were in favor of using force and maybe robbery. Murdock stoutly opposed this, and for the time succeeded in preventing his followers from doing anything rash.

However, he fell ill; so ill that he had to stop. He could not travel farther until he was better. But his men wanted to keep going, and the caravan leader would not consent to even a halt. Fearing the worst, but seeing no way of preventing it, he dropped out and watched the caravan rumble on up the trail.

It was the last time he ever saw any of them. For three days he was unable to travel, and when he did start he had to go slowly. Four days' riding brought him to the wrecked caravan. There had been a battle. Evidently the guides had attempted to rob the caravan, and had succeeded. He found the bodies of the Austrian and his drivers where they had been buried, and nearby he located loot which they had captured. Some of it they had evidently taken with them, but there was not room for all. And a fabulous fortune it was; gold, jewelry, and other treasures, belonging to the Emperor Maximilian. Murdock made a map of the region and hastened on down the trail that his companions had taken.

Three days later he found them, too. The Comanches had ambushed them and killed every man. Their scalped bodies remained where they had fallen; some of the loot they had taken from the caravan lay beside them. Their horses were gone: this was probably what the Indians had been after, Murdock reflected. There were evidences that a renegade white man was with the Indians and leading them, but for some reason he had overlooked part of the plunder.

Murdock carried the treasure back to the scene of the caravan battle, and buried it all together,

keeping out only as much as he could carry on his horse. Then, carefully guarding his map of the place, he slowly made his way to San Antonio. Apparently he planned to get a wagon and team and come back for his treasure, but he never got back. Fresh outbreaks of Indian troubles, homesickness, the loss of his companions—these probably influenced him to decide to go back to his old home. So, instead of going on to Mexico, one summer morning he set his face toward Missouri. Doubtless he would return later.

On the road between Fort Worth and Denton, Texas, he camped one night with a group of strangers. He asked them few questions and accepted their invitation to eat and sleep with them. Before daylight he was aroused by a posse of hard-faced men; and by the time he was fully awake he found himself under arrest as the member of a gang of horse thieves. It did no good to protest that he did not even know his associates; he was arrested and lodged in the Denton County jail.

Almost immediately he again fell sick, but this time he did not recover. He did manage to get the jailer to call a doctor, who told him he was going to die. He also secured the services of a lawyer, who got him out of jail. But the only way he could pay his two friends was to give them the map of the treasure out in the Pecos region; his money had already disappeared or had been stolen. This he did, and in his last moments told them the story of the caravan and its end.

The doctor and lawyer, whose names are not revealed to us, made every effort to find the treasure. The lawyer secured an appointment as a federal judge in the Pecos area, and the doctor finally moved to a nearby town. Both of them, plus their friends and descendants, hunted many times for the cache. Traces of the old wagon tires were found, we are told, also some remains of the wagons themselves. The map indicated that the burial was at the edge of a small pond of water fed by a spring flowing out of the side of a hill. But drifting sand had erased all marks.

And thus far no one has ever found the treasure. Maximilian, of course, was captured and shot by the Juaristas. And his crown jewels and other treasures lie buried under some pile of sand near the Horsehead Crossing of the Pecos River.

It is not difficult to find the Horsehead Crossing. Apparently it is not on a modern highway, but it *is* on the Pecos River. It is about twenty miles northwest of the town of Girven, which is a mile or so off the main Highway 67, southwest of McCamey. It lies at the western end of a twelve-mile canyon known as Castle Canyon.

In the old days the crossing was famous as the first watering place going west for about ninety miles. John Butterfield operated a stage line over the Castle Canyon route before the Civil War. In 1866 Charles Goodnight and Oliver Loving drove a herd of cattle over the region, watering their almost-starved herd at the place. The trail, which followed up the Pecos, went on up into New Mexico from the Horsehead Crossing.

Many hunters have looked for the treasure, in widely scattered areas. There is a rough, rocky ridge some ten miles north and a little west of McCamey, Texas, where hunters for Maximilian's treasure have dug up hundreds of acres of ground. Natives of the area say that one party came all the way from Austria, searching for the treasure. Some hunters have gone so far as to blast into solid rock with dynamite.

Most of this digging has been done at the southern entrance to Castle Gap, a pass in the King Mountains, which are just south of Castle Mountain. The Old Chihuahua Trail leads through this pass, the same trail over which came salt-haulers from Mexico City to get salt from the lake deposits not far north of the King Mountains.

Perhaps they were on a warm trail; perhaps not.

If we are to believe the old yarn, the treasure lies buried in what was once a little stream flowing out of the side of a hill not far from the Old Horsehead Crossing.

Maybe somebody will find it some day. Maybe it is just a legend. *Quién sabe?*

Things to Do

1. Who was Maximilian? (You may need help from the library to answer this question.)
2. Why were Bill Murdock and his men going to Mexico to help him?
3. List the main events in the story. The first three should be:
   a. Bill Murdock and his friends decided to go to Mexico to help Maximilian.
   b. They met a train of ten wagons, drawn by mules and supposedly carrying a cargo of wool and hides.
   c. The caravan leader offered Murdock and his friends three hundred dollars each to escort them to San Antonio.
4. Give your reasons for thinking that this story is true or is another "tall tale".

The Open Range

The Longhorn Helped
to Build an Empire

Perhaps no other animal has had a more important part in the building of a nation than the Texas longhorn, behind whose thundering hoofs hardy pioneers rode to civilize the West.

Many are the tales of the longhorn's fierce nature, daring, and stamina. But more fascinating than any of these is the story of how he paved the way for the economic development of the West.

The beginning of the longhorn goes back more than four centuries, when Andalusian cattle were brought to Mexico by the Spanish conquerors. They were descendants of the stately longhorns introduced into Spain by the Moors.

The conquest of Mexico by Cortés was followed by the establishing of missions and fortresses all the way up to and across the Rio Grande into Texas. To the missions the early Catholic padres drove herds of longhorn cattle as a source of meat and milk.

The wild uninhabited region that stretches between the Nueces and the Rio Grande rivers in southern Texas, with plentiful grass and water, was a paradise for the longhorn. By 1830 this breed of cattle, brought into Texas from Mexico, had multiplied to over one hundred thousand head.

The longhorn's only menace in Texas was wild beasts — panthers, mountain lions, cougars, and wolves. But for these enemies nature had equipped him with ample protection. His horns were long and sturdy, and his hoofs were sharp. Using his horns and his hoofs, he could fight off the fiercest animals.

Until 1840 the longhorns roamed Texas as wild animals. The Republic of Texas declared them public property, allowing anyone to claim ownership who branded them.

During the War between the States, old men,

boys, and Negro slaves were left to look after the longhorns as best they could. There was little demand for their meat. The Mississippi River was captured by Federal troops, and Texas cattle therefore could not be supplied to the Confederate army. As a result, the longhorns continued to multiply. By the end of the war in 1865, they had increased to an estimated four million.

Returning from the battlefields, Confederate soldiers found their homes ruined, their farms and ranches run down, and their ranges overrun with wild longhorn cattle. The only money brought back home by the Southern soldier was Confederate money, then worthless. Poverty and desolation faced them on every side.

While there was little demand for the supply of cattle in Texas after the War between the States, there was a great demand for cattle in the industrial centers of the North and East. Texans had been informed that cattle were bringing fifty and sixty dollars a head in the far North. At home they were worth about $2.50 to $5.00 a head. If only their cattle could be moved to market, the financial troubles of Texas settlers would be over.

Several attempts were made to drive the cattle through to Missouri, but armed bands met the drivers and stole the cattle. Then Texans looked to a trail through the West, preferring to face the Plains Indians rather than armed marauders in the Central States.

J. G. McCoy of Indiana, a cattle dealer, saw the need of a rail connection for the Texans and their cattle. After many trials and tribulations he succeeded in establishing pens and rail facilities at Abilene, Kansas.

A man named Thompson is said to have driven the first Abilene-bound herd of cattle north from Texas, and on September 5, 1867, the first trainload of cattle was shipped from Abilene.

Soon a great industry was under way. Up the winding trails north from Texas during the next twenty years it is estimated that more than ten million cattle were driven to market and to pastures in the West.

Some of the cattle were very poor when they arrived in Kansas. These were herded out on the plains to fatten, and thus opened up another chapter in the longhorn's history. Out on the western plains to Kansas, Colorado, North and South Dakota, Oklahoma, and New Mexico a steady stream of longhorns went their way as they spread into other states. Many of them went as far north as Canada.

Settlers and farmers followed the longhorn's trail, and where the settlers went the railroads followed. In the short space of fifteen years the longhorn had done more to open up and civilize the West than had been done by all the other forces in the past years. His hides and his meat brought ready cash to a wide section of the country made poor by war. He served as the first economic tie to rebuild a bankrupt people.

For a quarter of a century, prior to 1890, the longhorn ruled the cattle industry west of the Mississippi River. Then, his purpose served, his destiny at an end, he faded out of the picture. The progress he helped to bring about turned against him.

It was no longer necessary to drive cattle a thousand miles to market, for railroads were built into the Southwest to transport them. Prices of longhorns advanced. Then cattlemen looked to better breeds. They needed cattle with more flesh and less muscle, more weight and less bone. As a result, cross-breeding the Hereford with native cattle crowded out the lanky longhorn.

Today there are but a few of the real longhorns left in the National parks. His descendants dot the plains and hills, but the original plains longhorn has vanished. He has gone the way of the covered wagon, the muzzle-loading musket, and the coon-skin cap.

The National Park Service, however, is considering a plan to preserve the few longhorns that are left in the international park in the Big Bend country. Beneath the towering Chisos Mountain peaks the longhorn may stage a comeback, to future children who may see this rugged animal that has contributed so much to the upbuilding of the West.

— *Frontier Times*

Things to Do

1. Use a world map to show how the longhorn came to Texas.
2. In what part of Texas did the longhorn thrive? Why?
3. How did the longhorn protect himself from enemies?
4. How were cattle taken to markets in the north in the early days?
5. Why were longhorns found in Canada after 1867?
6. Why is the longhorn known as a trail-blazer?
7. Why do we not see herds of longhorns today? Where can you see a small number of these animals?
8. Give the meaning of this sentence: "The longhorn has gone the way of the covered wagon, the muzzle-loading musket, and the coonskin cap."
9. Why were cattle driven from Texas to Kansas rather than to Missouri?

The Zebra Dun
A Cowboy's Story

We were camped on the plains
    at the head of the Cimarron
When along came a stranger
    and stopped to arger some.
He looked so very foolish
    that we began to look around,
We thought he was a greenhorn
    that had just 'scaped from town.

We asked if he had been to breakfast;
    he hadn't had a smear,
So we opened up the chuck-box,
    and bade him have his share.
He took a cup of coffee
    and some biscuits and some beans,
And then began to talk and tell
    about foreign kings and queens.

Such an educated feller
    his thought just came in herds,
He astonished all them cowboys
    with them jaw-breaking words.
He just kept on talking
    till he made the boys all sick,
And they began to look around
    just how to play a trick.

He said he had lost his job
   upon the Santa Fe
And was going across the plains
   to strike the 7-Bar-D.
He didn't say how come it,
   some trouble with the boss,
But said he'd like to borrow
   a nice fat saddle hoss.

This tickled all the boys to death,
   they laughed way down in their sleeves,
"We will lend you a horse
   just as fresh and fat as you please."
Shorty grabbed a lariat
   and roped the Zebra Dun
And turned him over to the stranger
   and waited for the fun.

Old Dunny was a rocky outlaw
   that had grown so awful wild
That he could paw the white out of
   the moon every jump for a mile.
Old Dunny stood right still —
   as if he didn't know,
Until he was saddled
   and ready for to go.

When the stranger hit the saddle,
   old Dunny quit the earth

And traveled right straight up
    for all that he was worth,
A-pitching and a-squealing,
    a-having wall-eyed fits,
His hind feet perpendicular,
    his front ones in the bits.

We could see the tops of the mountains
    under Dunny every jump,
But the stranger he was growed there
    just like the camel's hump;
The stranger sat upon his back
    and curled his black mustache
Just like a summer boarder
    waiting for his hash.

He thumped him in the shoulders
    and spurred him when he whirled,
To show them flunky punchers
    that he was the wolf of the world.
When the stranger had dismounted
    once more upon the ground,
We knew he was a thoroughbred
    and not a gent from town.

The boss who was standing round
    watching of the show,
Walked right up to the stranger
    and told him he needn't go:

"If you can use the lasso like
    you rode old Zebra Dun,
You are the man I've been looking for
    ever since the year one."

Oh, he could twirl the lariat
    and he didn't do it slow,
He could catch them forefeet nine
    out of ten for any kind of dough.
And when the herd stampeded
    he was always on the spot
And set them to nothing,
    like the boiling of a pot.

There's one thing and a shore thing
    I've learned since I've been born,
That every educated feller ain't
    a plumb greenhorn.

— *Author Unknown*

Whoopee Ti Yi Yo, Git Along Little Dogies
A Cowboy's Song

As I walked out one morning for pleasure,
I spied a cow-puncher all riding alone;
His hat was throwed back and his spurs was a-jingling,
As he approached me a-singin' this song:
    Whoopee ti yi yo, git along little dogies,
    It's your misfortune, and none of my own.
    Whoopee ti yi yo, get along little dogies,
    For you know Wyoming will be your new home.

Early in the spring we round up the dogies,
Mark and brand and bob off their tails;
Round up our horses, load up the chuckwagon,
Then throw the dogies upon the trail.

It's whooping and yelling and driving the dogies;
Oh, how I wish you would go on;
It's whooping and punching and go on little dogies,
For you know Wyoming will be your new home.

Some boys goes up the trail for pleasure,
But that's where you get it most awfully wrong;
For you haven't an idea the trouble they give us
While we go driving them all along.

When the night comes on and we hold them on the bedground,
These little dogies that roll on so slow;
Roll up the herd and cut out the strays,
And roll the little dogies that never rolled before.

Your mother she was raised way down in Texas,
Where the jimson weed and sand-burrs grow;
Now we'll fill you up on prickly pear and cholla
Till you are ready for the trail to Idaho.

Oh, you'll be soup for Uncle Sam's Injuns;
"It's beef, heap beef," I hear them cry.
Git along, git along, git along little dogies
You're going to be beef steers by and by.

— Author Unknown

Cattle

Other states were carved or born,
Texas grew from hide and horn.

Other states are long or wide,
Texas is a shaggy hide.

Dripping blood and crumpled hair:
Some fat giant flung it there.

Laid the head where valleys drain,
Stretched its rump along the plain.

Other soil is full of stones,
Texans plow up cattle-bones.

Herds are buried on the trail,
Underneath the powdered shale;

Herds that stiffened like the snow,
Where the icy northers go.

Other states have built their halls,
Humming tunes along the walls.

Texans watched the mortar stirred
While they kept the lowing herd.

Stamped on Texan wall and roof
Gleams the sharp and crescent hoof.

High above the hum and stir
Jingle bridle-rein and spur.

Other states were made or born,
Texas grew from hide and horn.

— *Berta Hart Nance*

Driving Texas Cattle to Kansas

As we watch big diesel engines pulling dozens of cattle cars across Texas, it is difficult for us to remember that cattle were once driven to markets hundreds of miles away. They were driven across unfenced country to the nearest railroads in Kansas. This is the story of a man who helped to drive cattle to Kansas seventy-five years ago.

In the spring of 1868 two men from Illinois by the names of Coolley and Grimes came into Coryell County and bought a herd of beef cattle at $10 a head, gold, and I consider they were a fine lot of beeves. None were under five years old. They were branded out at W. W. Hammack's pen, two and one-half miles from Gatesville. The road brand of this herd was Circle G on left loin. Cattle driven up the trails were known by the road brand in those days.

They were run into a chute made of heavy timber with cross bars at the top to keep them from spreading. Big fires were made near the chute, branding irons were placed in them to get hot. Two or three men were on top to apply the hot irons, and you had better know that those big old wild beeves would roar and snort when the hot iron was stuck to them. * * *

We left Gatesville on May 12, 1868, with the Coolley and Grimes herd. John G. Tompkins was

our boss, and the hands were Will and Henry Tolliver, Bill Elam, Taylor Hammack, Tom Pollard, Eli, George and Josh Franks, and a negro boy[1] (Hite Carden's negro). Wiley Adams was the cook.

I shall never forget the first stampede. It was on the night after we had crossed the Brazos River at old Fort Graham, about five or six miles out on the prairie. We camped on a branch with the chuck wagon; part of the boys were with the herd, while the others were in camp playing cards, when we saw a cloud rising in the northwest. We rounded up the cattle, caught our night horses, after we had eaten supper. The boss called out for us to get busy for

[1]Now the custom is to begin the name of a race with a capital letter.

there was going to be a storm, and the rain began pelting down. We were in front of the cattle, and they were drifting; it was dark, we could only see when the lightning flashed, and the thunder was big and loud, and I knew there was a boggy branch in front of us.

Just before the cattle commenced running there was a big clap of thunder and a long stroke of lightning, and seeing the branch just in front I began to bear to the right, but the cattle started to run. You could not hear anything, then I knew I was in a stampede and they ran and kept running. I thought of all my past life, of the mavericks I had stolen, of the watermelons I had pulled from old man Haygood, Bill Enyer and others. Anyway, I got out somehow. I never knew how. * * *

We crossed Red River twelve miles from Sherman; this was the lower route through the Indian territory. The grass was fine, and there were lots of fish in the streams, plenty of deer, turkey and all kinds of wild game. We never saw any buffaloes or wild Indians. We crossed the Arkansas River at the Creek Agency and traveled up the north side until we came in sight of Fort Wichita. There was nothing there then but one log cabin and some Indian tepees on the banks of the Arkansas River where the city of Wichita now stands. However, before we got there we had to cross a big creek named Walnut, and where the cattle trail crossed Walnut stands the town of Coffeyville today.

After leaving Wichita we traveled due north to Abilene, Kansas, stopping on a creek by the name of Bear. The chuck wagon camped under a big cottonwood tree on the banks of the creek where today stands the town of Newton, Kansas.

A bunch of Osage Indians came to our camp one day. They looked bad but seemed to be very friendly. One side of their heads was shaved as slick as a peeled onion.

On the trip I spoke of in 1868, Kansas had just begun to settle. . . Abilene was on the Smoky Hill River thirty-five or forty miles west of Junction City, Kansas. There was but one hotel in Abilene and it was called the Drovers Cottage. When we left Abilene we followed the railroad down to Junction City, then traveling down the Neosho River.

Council Grove was a noted place at that time, being at one time a place where several tribes of Indians met to hold their annual councils. There was at that time a tribe of Indians called the Kaw living down the Neosho River below Council Grove. The Government had built them nice little rock houses on land that was considered as fine as any in the State of Kansas, but weeds had almost taken their homes. There were just a few of the old ones left, as I remember; most all of them had left their homes and camped on some high hills northeast of Council Grove. We could see their tepees from the road we were traveling. Some of the spies who were on the lookout came to us and asked us if we had seen any Cheyennes. It seemed that the Cheyennes had sent them word that they were coming down and clean up on them. . . . I never learned whether the Cheyennes came or not.

We traveled down through middle Kansas, . . . crossed the Arkansas River just above Fort Gibson, . . . We crossed the Red River twelve miles from Sherman, ... We returned home all o. k. in July.

— *J. M. Franks*

Things to Do

1. On a map of the United States, trace the routes that were taken to Kansas and return.
2. Make a frieze showing the cattle drive. Your scenes may include the preparation for the drive, Indian visits, the stampede, and other activities.

Lost: Five Thousand Cattle

It was so hot, that October day in 1872, that the herd of five thousand cattle was panting at sundown, and the horses of the cowboys were wet with sweat. Jake Loner dismounted and waved a hand to the other cowboys.

"Round 'em up and bed 'em down, boys," he said. "It's only ten miles to the mouth of Terlingua Creek and the Rio Grande, and we've got the winter ahead of us."

No one objected to the order, but one cowboy did something that only newcomers or foolish folks did; he prophesied the weather. "It's too hot, even

for the Big Bend country," he said, eyeing the sky. "It's going to come some kind of weather."

It did come, about midnight. Its arrival was announced by continuous flashes of lightning that made the landscape almost as bright as day at times, and thunder heads rolled up across the northern sky. Then the clouds came nearer, and a fierce biting wind struck the camp of cowboys. The rain came in sheets; the herd stirred, began milling, and finally stampeded. Between intervals of lightning, it was so dark that a man could not see his hand before his face.

"Let 'em go, boys," ordered Jake. "We'll round 'em up tomorrow. Anyhow, we've got to prepare to take this blizzard, or we'll all freeze."

The outfit had a lone tent, which was hurriedly stretched. They were lucky enough to be near a ravine with a windbreak to the north, in which they staked their ponies. They even managed to drag in some rain-soaked dead mesquite wood which they coaxed into a blaze. Three of them slept in the chuck wagon, and all of them found it necessary to add their horse blankets and slickers to the usual rolls in order to keep warm.

The water turned to ice and the rain to snow. For four days, Loner and his men struggled to keep from freezing. It was not until the storm abated and the weather grew warmer that they gave much thought to their herd of cattle. It was the worst blizzard that the country had ever known.

When they did look for their herd, they failed to find it. They scoured the country for miles in every direction, but not a sign of the five thousand cattle could they see. The rain and snow had been so heavy as to wipe out tracks, but not even a frozen carcass could they locate. So far as they could tell, those cattle had vanished from the earth.

They could not even guess what had become of the herd. Some of them thought the animals had drifted into the river and been drowned. That was possible, for the Rio Grande was half full of water. They had to give up that theory, though, after going miles down the river on both sides and finding not a single carcass.

They wondered if rustlers had driven the cattle across the river and into the interior of Mexico, but in that case they surely would have left some kind of trail. To satisfy themselves, Loner and his men scouted the country south of the river — but found nothing. For two weeks they searched before they gave up.

The story was told and retold around chuck wagon fires until it became a legend. In time many came to regard it as a "tall" tale. Others were curious enough to visit the place where the herd was supposed to have been lost, but always they came away shaking their heads. Still others hunted up survivors of the expedition and heard the tale afresh. But no one could figure out what had become of the herd.

Some fifty years later, two prospectors entered the Terlingua Creek region. They had heard of a silver mine there that the Spaniards had operated in the old days, and they wanted to find it. L. B. Bertillion, one of the men, had heard also the tale about the lost herd of cattle.

Sundown found them in the upper end of a long, narrow canyon. As they needed water and a camping place, they pushed on down the canyon. It grew deeper, and its sides became steeper as they rode south. Finally they reached the lower end only to find a wall of rock facing them. But there was an opening in the rock, and the men cautiously dismounted to take a closer look.

"A cave!" muttered Bertillion's companion, "and a big one at that."

"And some bones!" replied Bertillion, "and horns. Looks like an old-time longhorn must have worn them."

They camped and waited till morning, when they explored the cave at length. It covered several acres and was filled with many tons of bones and horns, some in a good state of preservation.

There was no doubt in their minds, nor was there any in the minds of others who went to see the cave. For all who knew the story, the fifty-year-old mystery had at last been solved.

—*J. A. Rickard*

Things to Do

1. Write answers to the following "why" questions. Look back at the story for the answers that you do not remember:
   a. Why did Jake Loner tell his cowboys to let the cattle go when they stampeded?
   b. Why did the cowboys not think about the cattle for four days?
   c. Why did some of the men think that the cattle had drowned?
   d. Why were they confident that rustlers did not drive the herd into Mexico?
   e. Why did the story of the lost herd finally become a "tall" tale?
   f. Why did prospectors enter Terlingua Creek fifty years later?
   g. Why were these men sure that the lost herd had been found?

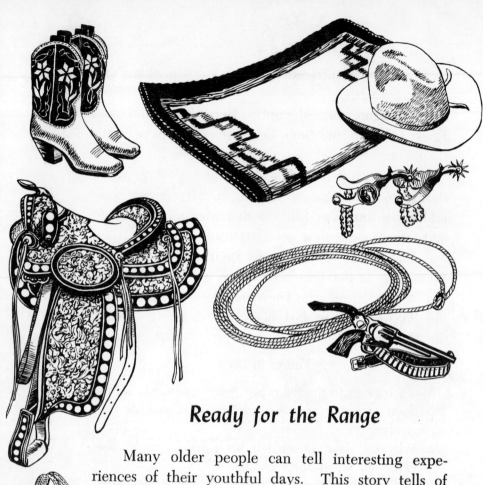

Ready for the Range

Many older people can tell interesting experiences of their youthful days. This story tells of plans and preparations made by a boy for a summer vacation many years ago:

When I was a boy — I was going to be twelve that summer — people living in towns sometimes allowed their sons who were old enough, to work for a rancher or farmer during vacation. Usually, the man was a friend of the family, and could be depended upon to take good care of the boys, give them helpful outdoor training, and pay them for their work. The chores were never too hard, and the boys always looked forward to a summer on a ranch. A friend of my father's, a Mr. Mason, had asked for me that year.

School had been out a week before Mr. Mason finally came to town. I was beginning to be pretty anxious by the time he came riding up to our gate late one afternoon, leading a horse for me to ride home with him. He left both horses in our barn and went to spend the night with relatives nearby, telling me that I should be ready to start out early the next morning.

My sister, Julia, almost as excited as I was about the trip, offered her help with the packing. In those days, girls stayed home with their mothers, but Julia thought living on a ranch would be fun, and wished she could go along. I promised to tell her all about everything when I came home.

Deciding which of my clothes and other possessions to take along was hard to do since this would be my longest absence from home.

"Of course," I told Julia, "I won't wear exactly what the regular hands do, like a pistol, or a cartridge belt, or a holster, but I'll carry my .22 rifle when I go out on the range or ride fence. That's the way they do on ranches because there's no telling where a rattlesnake or a wolf or a ringtail cat will be."

Once I killed a bobcat with the gun given me at Christmas time; and now I was sure that I would be an experienced hunter after a summer on the range! So, my gun was the first thing we put out to take along.

After supper was over, my mother said that I must retire early, so I'd be rested for the long ride the next day. Julia would help her to pack my clothes. I could hear them talking long after I was in bed —

"Carl can wear his father's pants since we cut them down. These shirts are still good, too. There's lots of wear left in them."

"Pack the pants and shirts and other clothes in Pa's saddle-bags. Here's a vest he can take, too, the one your brother Bob left when he went to Wyoming. Carl will be happy to wear it open like the men do. There! That's everything now, except his coat. If we have an early fall, he'll need it on the way home."

It didn't require a second call to awaken me the next morning. Ma had ready all the clothes I was to carry, and Pa had my plate filled with fried potatoes, grits, bacon, and eggs by the time I had finished dressing.

"This is the kind of breakfast you will have every morning on the range," Pa said, as he filled a glass with milk from a pitcher. "And it always tastes better from the chuck wagon. Mr. Mason tells me that you will soon be learning what a real cowboy's life is like. He is late with the spring roundup this year, but as soon as that is over, he wants you to go with the boys to take the cattle to their summer range."

At a Rodeo.

"How far is it to Mason's ranch?" asked my uncle, who was visiting us from Fort Worth.

"Only about twelve miles to his home ranch, but nearly seventy to the summer range," Pa explained, as we finished breakfast.

"Carl, I have a surprise for you. Since you will be away on your birthday, I'll give it to you now. It is a hat, just your size, and should fit you well. You will need it for your trip," my uncle said.

"Say, Carl," Pa said, "you know, a cowboy takes special pride in his hat. Sometimes it costs him a month's wages."

I was so proud of that hat; it was exactly what I'd wished to own for a long time — a "genuine beaver" of heavy gray felt! Pa and Uncle helped to push in the crown and admired the leather hat-band and buckle.

"That hat will last for a long time — and you will find many uses for it besides shading you from the sun and rain," Pa told me. "I have used mine for a pillow, for a basket to carry quail's eggs in, and even for a bucket for carrying water. When the wind is cold, I have tied it over my ears with a bandanna!"

"Oh, I have a present for you too, Carl," Julia said, "a red bandanna!" She folded the big, bright-colored square diagonally, then tied it around my neck as the others smiled their approval. "This is really the best way to tie it," she explained, " 'cause you can let it hang down in front to keep you from blistering in the hot sun, or pull it over your nose and mouth when you are riding in the dust."

"Yes, a cowboy would be lost without a bandanna," my uncle said. "The men you will live with this summer will show you many new ways to use it."

When I had admired my new hat and bandanna in the dining room mirror, I turned to thank Uncle and Julia — and there was my mother coming through the door with something in her arms!

Smilingly she handed me a pair of chaps, a slicker, a quirt of plaited leather — and some spurs!

"Pa and I will just have to give you the presents we have, too — a whole week before your birthday! With your boots that you have kept shined so well, you will be the best dressed cowboy on the range! Try them on now, so we can all see how they fit," Ma said quickly, when she saw how surprised I was.

"The slicker is not used often," Pa said, "but when it does rain, or when the wind blows cold, it is certainly appreciated. You can wear it as well on horseback as you can when walking. I'll show you how to tie it on the back of your saddle, where it is always ready when needed."

Julia thought the chaps the best present of all. They were made of goatskin, and came almost to the floor. "Now if you only had a pistol and holster," she said, "you would look just like a cowboy I saw in town one day."

"The quirt is mostly ornamental," Pa laughed. "I wouldn't try using it for awhile — not till you learn to ride well enough to break wild horses, anyway. I don't believe I've ever seen a cowboy use one, even for that."

"The spur is almost a part of a cowboy's boot," Uncle added, as he watched me buckle a strap. "With those leather straps over the foot and under the high heel, cowboys usually just leave the spurs fastened when they take their boots off."

Then Pa said: "Don't forget, Carl, that the cowboy's saddle is important. It is heavy and strong enough to stand the wear and tear of riding and roping, but it can bruise the horse's back if not put on with the saddle blanket carefully smoothed out. And be sure to remember that the cowboy's pony is his best pal and always receives the kindest treatment."

By the time I finished adjusting straps on my chaps and spurs, and had thanked everyone for my cowboy equipment, Mr. Mason was knocking on the front door. Pa and Uncle helped me with the saddle, then tied my saddle-bags on the back with my slicker. Hanging the quirt on the horn, I was ready to mount and ride away, well equipped for a memorable summer on the range.

— *J. A. Rickard*

Things to Do

1. Cowboys have a very special kind of equipment for their job. Copy the list of equipment below and write beside the name of each the special way in which cowboys use it:

a. boots	h. pistol
b. spurs	i. stirrup
c. chaps	j. saddle
d. bandanna	k. quirt
e. gloves	l. rope
f. hat	m. horse
g. slicker	

Camels in Texas

Did you know that a large herd of camels was brought to Texas a hundred years ago? The writer of this story was Lieutenant Governor before the Civil War and was also the Governor of Texas from 1861 to 1863. He supervised the care of some of the camels on his ranch and here tells of his interesting experiences with these queer looking animals.

At this period I had a strange experience in the stock business with a lot of camels intrusted to my care.

Old Texans remember that under the leadership of the Honorable Jefferson Davis, when Secretary of War, a cargo of thirty or thirty-five camels were landed at Indianola in the spring of 1856. After a short rest in that vicinity they were driven to San Antonio. A few weeks later the herd went into permanent quarters at Camp Verde, thirty miles northwest of that city. They were in charge of Major Wayne, who tested with satisfactory results their ability as swift burden bearers. The next spring forty more were landed at Indianola, and they joined the other herd at Camp Verde.

In the fall of 1858 a couple of ships, presumably British, anchored at Galveston under suspicious circumstances. They were at first thought to be

"slavers" watching for an opportunity of secretly landing their human freight. But the ships turned out to be loaded only with camels. At least no evidence appeared that they had any African Negroes aboard to sell as slaves.

Happening to be in Galveston at that time, I went to see the camels after they had been landed and penned. Mrs. Watson, an English lady, owner of the herd, was hunting some reliable person to whom she might intrust their care till they were finally disposed of, by sale or otherwise. I was introduced as a proper person to the lady and to her

agent, Señor Michado. After arrangements were made as to the extent of my obligations for their safety, I contracted with Señor Michado to take care of the camels delivered at my ranch. Accordingly a steamboat was chartered, on which Michado brought the animals to the mouth of Sims' Bayou for delivery.

The landing took place in the presence of a crowd of spectators, among whom were Sam Allen, Jules Barron (my brother-in-law), and myself. On finding themselves once more on solid ground, the camels showed their high spirits by rearing and frisking about like sheep. Observing these capers, Barron remarked that he did not believe that anyone could lasso a camel. Allen quickly said it could be done and bet Barron ten dollars that he could rope one himself.

Allen mounted his horse, lasso in hand, and with a sharp swing, on the first trial threw it over the head of a large camel and brought him to the ground after a short struggle. Barron, lately from Louisiana, had not learned that Texans generally accomplish what they undertake. Michado, with his outlandish servants, Turks or Arabs of unpronounceable names, conducted the camels to my ranch, a few miles distant. Here they were easily corralled in the pasture prepared for them.

Once the camels were in my care, Michado returned to Galveston, leaving the herd with the foreigners, whom I will call "Arabs." The pasture had in it seventy-five acres or more, nearly all prairie, with a small skirt of timber near the bayou, and enclosed by a new staked and ridered fence. In addition to grazing in the enclosure, there was given them every day large quantities of cured hay, which they ate at will.

Every two or three days, when it was warm, they were taken out of the pasture to water at a selected place on the bayou, to avoid bogging. In winter they were watered every four or five days. This was managed with so much care that only one or two camels bogged at the watering place. These had to be drawn out of the bayou by a yoke of strong oxen;

for after several unsuccessful attempts to get themselves out and getting deeper in the mire, they sank down quietly, with only a few mournful cries of distress, apparently resigned to their fate.

And it was not without some nursing and attention that they fully recovered from their sad experience on being hauled out. While he is not perhaps so much of a water animal as the horse, the camel can certainly swim, as was shown by some of this herd in Buffalo Bayou. I remember having lost but one from the effects of bogging.

This herd did not seem to suffer from cold in the winter of 1858-59, although they had no protection but a skirt of timber on the north. The ration of each camel was eight or ten pounds of hay each day in winter, when there was practically no grazing in their pasture. While he was especially fond of small grain such as wheat, barley, and oats, the camel when hungry will browse on any kind of shrub and seem to like it.

As to their powers of endurance and traveling ability I had no sure proof. But I have been told by those who know that, in a pinch, they can travel a week without food or water, carrying 300 or 400 pounds each. I have also been told that the dromedaries, or "the coursers of the desert," can travel fifty miles a day with a burden of 150 pounds.

While the general disposition of the camel is meek, the males at a particular season of the year are very fierce, and sometimes fight each other to the death. The camels in my charge appeared healthy and free from all disease, unless something on the skin like the itch might be so considered. During their year's stay at my ranch, besides one lost in the bog, only two died, and that from causes unknown.

The camels were naturally a great curiosity for Texans, and our neighbors, and people from a distance flocked in to see the strange sight. The camels were quite obedient to their Arab keepers, kneeling and rising at word of command. In going to Houston, six miles distant, the Arabs would ride a camel each, and their entry and exit would always create a sensation among the people of the town who saw them for the first time.

— *Francis Richard Lubbock*

Things to Do

1. Using a world map, find the places where camels live. Why did the U. S. Secretary of War in 1856 think that camels might be useful in Texas? The map should help you decide the answer.
2. Make a list of the facts about camels that you learned from the story.
3. Which do you think is easier to lasso, a camel or a steer?
4. Illustrate the last paragraph in the story. Share your illustration with your classmates.

The Settlers Came

Life in a Frontier Town in 1858

Modern inventions have so changed living conditions
that it is difficult to realize how people lived a century
ago. This selection describes living conditions in early
El Paso. Many of these conditions were the same in
other places throughout the Southwest. The story is told
by a man who lived in El Paso almost a hundred years
ago.

Those Who Came

Of the Americans then at El Paso, some had
left wives, or debts, or crimes behind them in "the
States," and had not come to the frontier to teach
Sunday school. But there were good people here
also, and for the few who were capable of doing
business and willing to work, the opportunities were
as good then and as profitable as they have ever
been since that time. The products of the mines,
crudely worked, in northern Mexico, were brought
to El Paso and exchanged for merchandise or money.

The military posts (forts) in northwest Texas and southern New Mexico were supplied with corn, flour, beef, hay, fuel, etc., by El Paso merchants and contractors.

The Overland Mail Company then operated a weekly line of mail coaches, drawn by six animals, between St. Louis and San Francisco. The time between these two cities was usually twenty-six days, the distance being 2600 miles. These splendid Concord coaches. . .carried the United States mail, for a government subsidy, and usually four to nine through passengers, besides the driver and "conductor." Changes of animals were made at "stations" built of rock or adobe, every twenty-five to forty miles, or wherever the company could find a stream, or spring, or waterhole. These coaches traveled day and night, in all kinds of weather.

El Paso was at this time (1858) the terminus of two other important stage routes — one from Santa Fe, New Mexico, and the other from San Antonio, Texas. These were in every particular so similar to the greater "Overland" route that a description is unnecessary. There was also a stage line to Chihuahua. . . .

In order that the importance of these mail routes and other enterprises on this frontier may be appreciated, I must here state a fact which may seem strange to some of my readers. At that time this whole frontier was in the actual possession of savage Indians. The Americans and Mexicans were secure only near the military posts, or large settlements, and when they traveled from place to place, they traveled in companies strong enough for defense, or at night and by stealth, trusting to Providence, or luck, each according to his faith.

The men who, for whatever reasons, had made their way to this distant frontier, were nearly all men of character; not all of good character, certainly, but of positive, assertive individual character, with strong personality and self reliance. (The weaklings remained at home.) Many of them were well-bred and of more than ordinary intelligence, and had the manners of gentlemen. They were neither assassins nor thieves nor robbers. Vices? Plenty; but they were not of the concealed or degrading kind. Violence? Yes, but such acts were usually the result of sudden anger or of a feeling that under the conditions then existing each man must right his own wrongs or they never would be righted. Their ideas of right and wrong were peculiar, but they had such ideas nevertheless. . . .

Common dangers and trials united the two races as one family, and the fact that one man was a Mexican and another an American was seldom mentioned, and I believe seldom thought about. Each man was esteemed at his real worth, and I think our estimates of each other's characters were generally more correct than in more artificial societies.

Spanish was the language of the country, but many of our Mexican friends spoke English well,

and often conversations, and even sentences, were amusingly and expressively made up of a blending of words or phrases of both languages. . . .

General Living Conditions

The people, the peasantry, were contented and happy. To them, with their simple wants, it was a land of plenty. . .Our currency was the Mexican silver dollar, then at par, and the Mexican ounce, a gold coin worth sixteen dollars.

There were no banks, and no drafts or checks except those given out by the paymasters and quartermasters of the United States army.

Everybody loaned money when he had it, but only for accommodation. I knew of only one man in the whole valley who loaned money at interest or required security.

It was no unusual thing for merchants to loan large quantities of their goods, bales of print and muslin and sacks of sugar and coffee to their neighbor merchants, to be repaid in kind when their wagon train arrived.

Carriages and buggies were considered almost as community property, and the man who refused to lend them was considered a bad neighbor.

Everybody had credit at "the store," and everybody paid up — sooner or later.

There were no hotels. Travelers stopped at each other's houses and even strangers were welcome there. Anyone having any claim to gentility or education was cheerfully received and entertained by the officers at the army posts, and many, very many, by the collector of customs at El Paso. . . .

Our merchandise and supplies were brought from St. Louis, a distance of sixteen hundred miles, or from Port Lavaca, Texas, a distance of nine hundred miles, by large trains of immense freight wagons, "schooners of the plains," drawn by fourteen to eighteen mules, usually four abreast, at a cost of twelve and one-half to fifteen cents per pound for freight only. These trains were usually accompanied by twenty-five to forty men, including the drivers, all of whom were well armed, and stood guard like soldiers.

The "wagonmaster" was a character of importance and authority, and a hunter was usually employed to procure fresh meat and to look out for Indian "signs." These trains, like the stage coaches, were often attacked by the Indians, but because of the greater number of men and better means of defense, they were not so frequently "taken in" as the latter.

I quote here the prices of a few of the articles purchased by me of El Paso merchants during the "sixties," having preserved the original bills: One common No. 7 kitchen stove, $125; ham and bacon, 75 cents per pound; coffee, 75 cents per pound; sugar, 60 cents per pound; lard, 40 cents per pound; candles, 75 cents per pound; one-half ream letter paper, $4; nails, 50 cents per pound; matches, 12½ cents per box; tobacco, $2 per pound; calico (print), 50 cents per yard; bleached muslin, 75 cents per yard; unbleached muslin, 50 cents per yard; coal oil, $5 per gallon; alcohol, $8 per gallon; lumber, rough sawed, 12½ cents per foot; empty whiskey barrels, $5 each; starch, 50 cents per pound.

But if we paid high prices, we also received high prices for what we had to sell. I made large quantities of wine from the El Paso grape, and sold it readily at $5 per gallon, $200 per barrel of forty gallons. For two years I furnished the government with all the vinegar and salt used in the military department of New Mexico, vinegar at $1.70 per gallon, and salt at 17 cents per pound, delivered at El Paso. The vinegar was manufactured from the El Paso grape, and the salt was brought from a natural lake, one hundred and twenty-five miles northeast of El Paso, and ground at Hart Mills, near El Paso, and sacked there. . . .

Profits were often great, and risks were always great. I do not think the desire for money, for its own sake, was as strong as in older communities, and this led to what we call liberality and what the wise call extravagance. If any man had devoted all his energies to accumulating and hoarding money he would have been viewed with disfavor by his neighbors, and at that time men were in many ways dependent upon the good will of their fellows.

Within the memory of men still living there occurred an incident which illustrates men's views of law and order in those days. A certain desperado had been getting drunk and riding into stores and saloons and firing his pistols at random in the streets and threatening people's lives, till the "good citizens" became weary. Finally he took a snap shot at the popular member of the legislature, Mr. Jeff Hall, on the main street. This was too much. In a few moments fifteen or twenty of the aforesaid "good citizens" were chasing him over town with shotguns, rifles, and pistols. The desperado was brought to

earth in the corral of the old Central Hotel. . .pierced
by many missiles. Then there was an animated
dispute among the above-mentioned good citizens
as to who had fired the fatal shot. One claimed
to have done the work with his shotgun. Another
said that such small ammunition at long range could
not kill such a man, but that it was his rifle shot in
the neck that did it. A third said that he had dis-
patched the deceased with three body shots from
his six shooter, and so on.

At last "Uncle Ben" Dowell said, "Gentlemen,
some day some judge or other may come along and

be holding court, and some of us may have trouble about this business." Thereupon they organized a coroner's jury, composed of the identical men who did the shooting, and sat upon the corpse and agreed upon a verdict, to the effect that "Deceased came to his death by gunshot wounds *from the hands of parties unknown. . . .*"

— *W. W. Mills*

Things to Do

1. Trace the routes of the mail coaches to El Paso at the time of this story. Also locate the route through which supplies were brought from Port Lavaca.
2. Choose sentences from the story that describe the character of the people. An example is this: "Many of them were well-bred and of more than ordinary intelligence, and had the manners of gentlemen."
3. Compare the prices of materials with the prices of the same things now.
4. What is your opinion of these frontiersmen's ideas of "law and order?"

The Gail Land Rushes

Located below the Cap Rock on the southeastern edge of the Staked Plains, the town of Gail is just a county seat. It is the only town in Borden County, Texas, and on its streets cattlemen and farmers gather to discuss work and weather. Oil wells form a more recent topic of discussion, for some have been drilled close by but, in general, all is quiet for the present.

But the past — ah, that's different. Old-timers are always eager to tell of Gail's early history, especially the story of the land rushes. They like to show visitors the old plank courthouse and the chute in the County Clerk's office down which went applications for land purchases.

When Texas entered the Union she kept the ownership of all unsold land in the state. Much of it was given to railroads to get them to build, but in 1876 other groups received donations. Two million acres went for a state university, three million to build a state capitol, and other large amounts were given to Confederate veterans, to counties, and to public schools. Some of this land was sold at a fixed price to the buyer who first deposited the money with the County Clerk on the day announced for sale. It was in two such sales that the Gail land rushes occurred.

They took place in 1904. Before that time ranchmen controlled the county, and every rancher had bought his limit of four sections of land from the state, plus all the other land nearby that he could buy. But the state still owned much land which the cattlemen were leasing until it should come on the market. When the local newspaper, the *Borden Citizen,* announced that on March 4 five sections of land would be sold, and that on March 11 three more sections would be sold, both cowmen and settlers determined to get it.

The settlers moved first. They occupied the

hall leading to the County Clerk's office. A day or two later, on February 29, a large number of cowboys came to town. Finding the foe weak in numbers, they organized, selected a captain, and pinned blue ribbons on their clothes. Then they attacked the red-ribboned settlers holding the court house door. Ten minutes later the last "red" picked himself up out of the dust in the court house yard. He glared at the "blue" foes now holding the door and went out to get help.

Three days later that help arrived. The "reds" came back to town with a large number of recruits. It took twenty minutes of pulling and fighting, but at the end of that time the last cowboy had been thrown out of the line. As the land came on the market the next day, the settlers got it.

Both sides made extensive preparations for the next land sale, which was to be held on March 11. The "blues" hired men from Abilene, Colorado, Big Spring, and other Texas towns. It was rumored that one cattleman was to bring three hundred hired men from Fort Worth. That the "reds" were just as busy was shown by the fact that they brought in help from ten Texas counties.

The "reds," or settlers, now had charge of the court house door, but by March 10 the blue-ribboned cowboys were ready to oust them. To prevent serious trouble, the sheriff made a talk to the crowd and announced some rules. First, he warned, there must be no violent fighting among them; but there was no rule against pushing or pulling. Second, he said, nobody must be armed, not even with a pocket knife. An obliging merchant offered the use of a large sugar barrel, and it was filled to overflowing with pistols, knives, and other weapons. Third, everybody who came over the plank steps leading into the court house yard had to be searched.

The crowd agreed to abide by these rules. At ten o'clock in the morning two hundred red-ribboned cowboys lined up for the job of ousting their foes. Led by a two hundred and forty pound giant, they pulled out the settlers one by one until none was left. Once they had control of the court house, the cowboys divided into three groups. One group stayed in the hall, a second group guarded the door, and the third group formed an outer ring of defense.

But the "red" settlers were not out for good. More of their friends kept coming in until by 2:00 P.M. they had about three hundred men ready for action. They, too, divided into three groups. The first two groups engaged the enemy at the door, while the third force made for the hall to drag out the "blues" from the door to the County Clerk's office.

The final grand attack came at three o'clock in the afternoon. The favorite method of attack was to get a foe to the ground and turn him over to two friends — one to each leg. For half an hour or more the milling, sweating, swearing crowd of over five hundred men fought it out. Sometimes friends would grab each other around the waist, so that the

foe had to pull fifteen or twenty instead of just one or two. Many a shirt was torn off, and much skin was lost before the battle was over.

The settlers finally won that contest and bought the land, but in reality both sides had been victors.

They had learned to settle serious differences according to law and without bloodshed. And they had a gloriously good time. Ask any old-timer who was present at the Gail land rushes to tell about them. A grin will appear on his face, and he is likely to begin with the words, "S-a-y, but that was *some* affair —"

And you might as well settle down to hear all the details.

— *J. A. Rickard*

Things to Do

1. Make a time line that shows events in the disposal of Texas public lands. Your line can begin like this:
   Jan. 20, 1854 — Sixteen sections of land offered for every mile of railroad built in the state.
2. Plan a dramatization of the Gail Land Rush. Your play may be given as a radio or TV show.

Thirty Dollars a Day for Sitting Still

The names in this story are not real, but the events actually occurred.

The spring roundup was over at the Bar D ranch, on the Texas South Plains, and Shorty Wilson, top cow-hand, was ready to take a vacation.

"Think I'll go to Midland," he said. "I see by the paper that the State of Texas is selling some land there in about two weeks. I might get a few sections and start a little ranch of my own — or become a squatter."

The other hands laughed at Shorty, but he carried out his threat. There were six others ahead of

him when he went to the court house, but he took a chair which the County Clerk courteously furnished, and prepared to sit it out.

The rules of the sale were printed in the daily paper, and he knew them. He understood that whoever was the first to file an application for the purchase of land on the day of the sale would have the privilege of buying as many as four sections. Since forty sections were to be sold, he would not be too late. Not more than twenty-four of them could be bought before his turn came. By some rare good luck, he had in his pockets enough money to make his purchase.

They were very obliging at the court house. They opened at eight o'clock in the morning and closed at six in the evening, and by common consent everybody kept the same seat in the line that he had the day before. That enabled Shorty to stay in a nearby hotel at night, where he could sleep and eat. Getting his noon meal was not so easy, but usually he could have a sandwich brought in at that time.

But he was not used to inaction, and the longer he sat in that seat, the harder it felt. He twisted and squirmed, but he could not leave. He could stand and stretch, and even walk up the hall. But he dared not leave the building, and he was afraid to leave his seat very long at a time. By the arrival of the tenth day, he was about ready to give up and quit, with only five more days to go.

Then there came into the hall a well dressed stranger, who looked up and down the line of chair sitters with a critical eye. He was trying to decide which sitter appeared most tired of sitting still. Finally, he cautiously approached Shorty.

"Want to sell your seat?" he asked.

Shorty pretended that he was not interested, and spoke of the immense value of the land that he was going to buy. However, in the end he admitted that he would sell anything he had if the price was high enough. Impressively, the stranger pulled out a roll of greenbacks, counted out and offered fifteen twenty dollar bills. Then and there, Shorty sold his chair and became a free man once more.

It was pretty hard for him to convince his partners at the old ranch that he was telling the whole truth and nothing but the truth when he told them what he had done. Fortunately, he was able to prove it by witnesses.

He was proud of that experience, and often he boasted about it. "Yes sir," he would say to anybody who would listen. "I've been paid fair wages for work, but that was one time when I got thirty dollars a day for sitting still."

— *J. A. Rickard*

Things to Do

1. How did Shorty make thirty dollars a day for sitting still? Plan to illustrate your answer with a dramatization.
2. Do you think that it was possible for a story like this to have happened in the days of "land rushes" in Texas? Why?
3. Read the parts of the story aloud that prove Shorty's cleverness.

Food for the Family

When your grandparents and great grandparents were children on Texas farms, there was one season of the year to which they looked forward eagerly: hog-killing time. Christmas, the Fourth of July, Thanksgiving — these were important, to be sure — yet to a farmer's family, none of them surpassed in importance the excitement of hog-killing day.

Providing food for the family was necessarily quite different from your mother's grocery shopping of today. Meat markets were few and far between.

The country had been settled to the extent that game animals were growing scarce, so that people had to raise their own meat or do without. Prolonged dry weather, a light cotton crop, and low cotton prices were discouraging to the farmer; but with a well-filled pigpen and enough corn nubbins to fatten the hogs, all might be well. The family could eat.

Hog-killing time was not just a one-day affair, for a wise farmer would not kill all of his animals at the same time. Usually he had a shoat for early meat and another one for a late cool spell. But the bulk of his hog-killing was done on a cold, clear day in January or February with a promise of some ice, or at least a heavy frost. All these were needed so he could leave the meat on the roof of the house at night until it was chilled through and through. This might mean two or three nights in succession. He wanted no rain, for that prevented the meat from "taking salt" well. He preferred a midweek day too: beginning on Friday or Saturday meant that there would be work on Sunday.

When the important day arrived, there was something for everyone to do. Sometimes the children were kept at home from school to help. Neighbors gathered to lend a hand, and always they were given "a mess of ribs" or a generous supply of backbone or liver. Whether they helped or not, they received some fresh meat, unless they too were killing hogs.

Organization for the Day

There was a definite division of work. The men and older boys prepared the scalding barrels, butchered the hogs, and scraped off the hair that had been loosened in hot water. The carcass was then hung by the hind feet to the limb of a tree, or to a previously prepared "scaffold," so that the insides could be removed. It was then placed on a large table to be cut into pieces: shoulder meat from the fore-legs, hams from the hind legs, and bacon from the sides.

The younger ones ran errands, kept fires going around the large water pots, and perhaps helped their parents at other tasks. The men and women made the sausage and stuffed it into sacks. The women rendered the lard and prepared the souse and scrapple, later making soap from the cracklings.

The children had the first taste of meat, for to them went the tails to roast in the very same fire that had heated the water. If they were put on early to cook, they were ready to eat long before the noon meal. This tasty "snack" was looked forward to as one of the main events of their day.

To be at their best, the tails had to be prepared carefully. They were scraped clean, and a goodly piece of lean meat was left on each thick end. Several damp pieces of paper were wrapped around every tail, or each was wrapped in mud and cov-

ered with hot ashes. Last of all, some red coals were placed on top of the ashes — and the tails were left to roast slowly for several hours.

"Quick" Pieces

Although most of the meat was to be salted and prepared for curing, some pieces, including the liver, had to be eaten at once, for it spoiled quickly. In the hands of a skilled cook, liver was a favorite meat for the hog-killing day dinner and could be sliced and fried or baked with onions and seasoning.

The spareribs were another hog-killing delicacy that had to be consumed early. If they were salted down with the larger pieces of meat, they became too salty and dry. To be at their best they had to be cut off with a generous amount of meat on them. After being properly seasoned, they were fried or smothered in a hot skillet or made into meat pies.

Because it too had so much bone and so little meat, the backbone, like the ribs, was used promptly. The housewife boiled, baked, or roasted it. When a well-cooked backbone was served on a large platter, flanked with baked sweet potatoes and accompanied with homemade catsup or chili sauce and hot biscuits — well, most farmers considered that a dish fit for any king!

The brains also had to be used without delay. These could be scrambled with eggs, and when served with hot bread and coffee, were as good at breakfast as they were for dinner or supper.

The hog's head and feet had to be used at once, too. They were cleaned, and cooked until the meat was quite tender. The bones were then removed, the meat seasoned and pressed to remove the excess liquid. This was called souse, and a tasty dish it made when sliced cold or rolled in corn meal and fried. Adding corn meal to the meat before it was pressed made a dish called scrapple.

But to many the most important work was the making of sausage. Most old-timers declare that modern meat market sausage does not compare with the kind the pioneers made. Perhaps they are correct, for the pioneers took great care in its making. They used the choice trimmings left after shaping the hams and shoulders, added the long strip of loin from near the backbone, and sometimes cut up a whole shoulder to add for good measure. They were careful to include about three-fourths lean and one-fourth fat in the mixture.

The fat and the lean meats were then put through the sausage grinder twice and mixed thoroughly. Most important of all was the seasoning, an all-family job. The housewife put in the salt, black pepper, red pepper, and sage — mixing a small amount with part of the ground meat. A sample patty was cooked, and now the sausage was ready to test! One at a time the children gleefully tasted it, the head of the house solemnly nibbled at it, and the cook took a final sample. If the combined verdict was "a little more sage," more was added. If it was "too much red pepper," some unseasoned meat was added. This continued until the flavor was just right.

The process of sacking followed. A piece of muslin cloth about three feet long and eight inches wide was sewed together along the sides and the bottom, turned with seam inside, and stuffed with sausage. The filled sacks were hung in the smokehouse, where later the hams, sides, and shoulders would be hung. Most of the sausage was eaten before summer, but sometimes it was cooked "rare" and packed in lard and preserved. This "summer sausage" was not as good as the fresh kind, however.

After these tasks had been completed, the lard was rendered; that is, pieces of fat were cooked slowly for many hours in an open kettle or iron wash pot. The substance had to be snowy white to satisfy its owners, for a single piece of lean meat was believed to discolor the whole pot. The housewife expected at least twenty gallons of lard from three or four large hogs. After the cooking, she strained it through cheese cloth or fine wire strainers and put it away in a cool place in tin or earthenware containers. It was regarded as superior to any "store-bought" shortening.

After the lard had been cooked and put away, many pieces of skin and other residue remained. Called "cracklings", some of these were made into soap by adding lye and water, and cooking. Some of the choicest bits were crumbled and used to make corn pone. This was the famous "cracklin' bread" that old-timers liked so well.

The final operation in the whole process was the smoking. After the meat had been buried in salt for several weeks, it was hung from the rafters of the smokehouse. An oak-chip or hickory wood fire was built and kept so low that it would never become a blaze, the door was closed, and the smoking was continued several days. Afterward, some of the meat was daubed with a paste of flour and sorghum, carefully wrapped, and left to hang.

The meat was gradually used as it was needed, but the housewife liked to have a ham left for use in the late summer when kinfolks made a visit, or the preacher called. Quite often, too, the farmer, assuming an indifferent air, took his neighbors to the smokehouse to show them the rows of hams, shoulders, and sides of bacon. He was proud of that, even to the point of bragging.

And well could he afford to be proud, for he had made a real achievement in the art of living. It gave him a feeling of solid satisfaction for which there was no substitute. Nothing could equal a well-filled smokehouse of juicy meat in midsummer.

— *J. A. Rickard*

Things to Do

1. Why was "hog-killing time" one of great excitement in the life of a pioneer family?
2. Select the main events in the story and list them in sequence. The first three events, in sequence, are as follows:
   a. The time chosen for butchering the hogs
   b. The division of work in butchering
   c. The roasting of the pigs' tails
3. Write your list on the blackboard. Compare it with your classmates' lists and use it to discuss the story.

Moving Onward

How the Railroads Came

Dr. S. O. Young, the author, lived in Houston when the first railroads were being built. In this story he describes the early days of railroading in Texas.

The first spade ever struck in the earth for the construction of a railroad in Texas was at Harrisburg away back yonder, as early as 1840. This was for the construction of the Harrisburg and Brazos Railroad, a line that was never built, at least not under that name.

Some grading was done and some ties were placed, but no iron was ever laid, and the enterprise was abandoned soon after it began. For eleven years the people of Harrisburg and Houston talked railroad, but they seemed to have wasted all their energy in talk, for they did nothing else.

However, in 1851, the line, which is now known as the Galveston, Harrisburg, and San Antonio, was actually begun at Harrisburg, and construction was pushed so vigorously that in nine years

eighty miles of road were actually built. In this
day of rapid transportation, when all the material
for railroad building can be obtained at almost a
moment's notice, it seems strange to hear that it
took nine years to build a crudely constructed line
of eighty miles.

That was rather rapid work for the early days,
though, for all the materials except the ties had to
be brought in sailing ships from Boston, New York,
or other ports of the Atlantic, unloaded at Galveston, and then brought up the bayou in steamships.

They were unloaded in Houston at a depot at Polk Avenue and San Jacinto Street, where all the cars stopped, but the locomotive would come down to San Jacinto and turn around and go into the engine house.

A lot of New Yorkers backed Abe Gentry, and he began the construction of the road to New Orleans. This road had money and credit too; and while it began construction later than the Houston and Texas Central and the Buffalo Bayou and Brazos railroads, when the Civil War broke out it had as much line constructed as either of them, and had trains running to Orange.

I don't suppose there ever were such railroads as those leading out of Houston became by the second and third years of the war. Schedules and time tables became farces. The trains came and went as they could, and they spent almost as much time off the tracks as on them. I remember on one occasion pulling out of Columbia on a train at the same time that a company of cavalry left there for Houston.

During the whole day we were never out of sight of that company. Sometimes we would be ahead, and sometimes they would lead. It was see-saw all day, and it took from early in the morning until dark to make the trip of fifty miles. Finally, just at dark, we reached Bray's Bayou and lost sight of the company. They had entered the woods ahead of us, however.

Before the close of the war all the roads except the Houston and Texas Central and the Galveston, Houston, and Henderson had ceased to run. In some way these two roads were kept in such a condition that they could still be used, but that was all. Using them was not a safe thing by any means. They crept along so slowly that while some wrecks occurred, it was a rare thing for anyone to get killed or even hurt.

I do not know what the reason for doing so was, but in those days the builders of locomotives always put immense smokestacks on them. The smokestacks were funnel shaped and several feet around at the top. They burned wood, and every few miles there were big stacks of cordwood piled along the track.

There was no such thing as spark arrestors, and every time the fireman put fresh wood in the box the passengers got the full benefit of the sparks, cinders, and smoke. It beat traveling by stage, however, and as the people knew nothing of oil burners, spark arrestors, and pullman cars, everybody was content.

The old-time fireman earned every dollar that he made, for he had to keep busy all the time. It was not child's play to have to keep up steam with only wood for fuel. Then too it took more steam to keep an engine going at that time, for the engineer was using his whistle ten times as often as he uses it now.

There were no fences along the right-of-way, and as there were thousands of cattle on the prairies and in the woods where the road ran, the track was generally filled with them every few miles. As soon as the trains would get out of the city limits the whistles would begin tooting, and this was kept up almost without stopping. Of course a great many cattle were killed, and this led to bitter warfare between the cattlemen and the railroads.

Wrecks and attempted wrecks were frequent, for there were not wanting men who, to get revenge on the railroad company by destroying its property, were willing to run the risk of destroying the lives of innocent passengers. The first wreck of this kind in Texas was on the Houston and Texas Central, about twelve miles from Houston. Some scoundrel drove spikes between the ends of the rails and wrecked the train. No one was killed, but Mr. Paul Bremond, who helped build the road and was on the train, received quite serious injuries and was laid up in bed for several days.

— S. O. Young

Things to Do

1. Did you think that parts of this story were humorous? Why?
2. Compare the locomotives that were used in 1840 with those now used.
3. Visit Harrisburg, now a part of Houston. You can locate the railroad that is described in the story.
4. Why was railroad building so slow in Texas before the Civil War?
5. What roads were built from Houston before the Civil War?
6. Why did trains often run so slowly and uncertainly?
7. What do you think of wood as a fuel for engines? Why?
8. Why were wrecks frequent?
9. Why was there trouble between the railroads and the cattlemen?

The Southern Overland Mail in Texas

We expect the postman to bring mail to our doors every day. Airmail letters from Thailand or South Africa do not surprise us. Less than a hundred years ago, men risked hostile Indians and death from lack of food and exposure in order to take mail across Texas!

Despite many hardships, men built mail and passenger routes across Texas. The old Butterfield Stagecoach route was the forerunner to modern railroads, highways, and skyways. It was a first step in conquering time and space in the Southwest.

When the United States acquired California in 1849, one of the first problems to solve was how to make contact with that distant possession. On March 3, 1857, Congress approved an act authorizing bids for a semiweekly mail service from some point on the Mississippi to San Francisco. The contract was awarded to John Butterfield and others.

The Southern route was selected, as it was passable at all seasons. It entered Texas at Colbert's Ferry, near Preston, on the Red River and passed in a west-southwestern direction of El Paso. The distance was 740½ miles, and the time schedule was eight days and nights. Butterfield was to receive $600,000 a year for four years for the service. The total distance of the route from Tipton, Missouri, to San Francisco was 2795 miles, to be made in twenty-five days. The rate of travel was five miles per hour, and the stations were about ten miles apart. The roads were unimproved, with streams to ford and mud holes to navigate. Speed was slowed to a walk in rocky or steep places.

The expense of establishing and equipping the entire route was about a million dollars. The route through Texas must have cost at least a third of that amount on account of supplying the stations and replacing stock stolen by Indians.

There were about ten men at each station. An agent, cook, stock tenders, water hauler, blacksmith, guards, and laborers made up the group. About one hundred Concord stages were used, that could carry nine inside, and were usually drawn by four horses or mules. At least one thousand head of horses and mules were constantly in use. Mules were used in the very dry stretches. They were generally the wild Mexican mules, that were hitched up blind-folded, and when they were turned loose they ran to the next station.

The gentle horses and mules were more easily stolen by predatory, plundering, Indians. The Co-manches stole 253 head of horses and mules in the winter of 1858-59. As most of the troops in Texas were dismounted, they were unable to overtake the mounted horse thieves.

The amount of mail was small, as few wanted to risk valuable mail. For the first quarter of the year that service was maintained, the waybills for passengers from San Francisco was only $12,000; which would be for east and westbound passengers about $200,000 per year.

In a pinch, fourteen passengers could be crowded on a coach, nine inside and five outside, in-cluding the driver. It had wide tires nearly as heavy as a prairie schooner's, a body slung on stout leather braces, and leather curtains. In the rear was a pro-tecting "boot," with leather cover for the twenty-five pounds of baggage allowed each passenger. The mail was always carried inside, even if a passenger was displaced, as mail had the right of way under the contract.

The halts were for only ten minutes; and meals

had to be eaten, other wants attended to, and sleep snatched when the coach was motionless. Passengers sometimes lost their minds through excessive heat, lack of sleep or rest, or fear of Indians, and had to be strapped in.

Each station had a cabin and a corral made of logs, stones, or adobe. Usually it was in the form of a quadrangle, or a square, large enough for the stage to drive in and turn around, with places for food for stock and passengers. On each side of the single gate was a room, the one for caretakers and the other for kitchen and storage. A few stations were known as "home stations." There, in addition

to the corral and haystack, was a house with an eating place, a blacksmith, and a wheelwright. In arid, or barren regions, tires would get loose through shrinking. . . .

The livestock had to be fed and watered in arid country, and where flash floods occurred, the stations had to be built high enough to avoid danger. Water, wood, and feed had to be hauled, so it kept caretakers constantly on the go, and they too were in danger of hostile Indians. In case of sickness or injury needing medical care they were out of luck. They would usually have to be taken to an army doctor at the nearest army post.

The total weight of the Concord coach loaded must have about equalled the loads we put on our U. S. Army Escort four-mule wagon on our trip into Mexico with General Pershing's expedition in 1916. We were allowed only 2,200 pounds per wagon, and the big army mules could not be driven faster than a walk.

One can therefore appreciate the speed made with the weight of the load carried by the Southern Overland Mail Line, and the courage and stamina of its drivers and caretakers.

— Frontier Times

Things to Do

1. Locate the old Butterfield Stagecoach route on an early map of the United States. Ask your teacher or librarian to help you to find other information about this old route.

2. Discuss facts about the following items in the story:
   a. The stations were ten miles apart.
   b. The route through Texas was expensive.
   c. Wild Mexican mules were used to pull the coaches in the very dry regions of the state.
   d. The mail sacks were carried inside the coach even if a passenger had to be displaced.
   e. Sometimes passengers became delirious.
   f. Ill passengers had to be taken to an army post.
3. Imagine that you were a passenger on a stagecoach crossing Texas. Write a story of your journey.
4. Make a collection of pictures of early stagecoaches, stations, etc. to share with your class.

The Overland Stage

Wild cavalcade of Indian raid
Along the lonely trail,
The savage pack is on the track
Of the plunging overland mail.
The stage coach rocks in the wagon ruts
Against the blood-red sun,
As over the hills the savage Sioux
On painted ponies run.

Before the Train traversed the plain
The travelers took the trail
On horse and mule and stage coach,
The Pony Express brought the mail.
They jogged and jolted and ambled on,
Or they rode wild and free
Through savage lands and Indian bands
Till they came to Fort Laramie.

— *James Daugherty*

Overland Freighting

The writer operated freight caravans between Texas and Mexico, after the American Civil War. His story gives a clear picture of the dangers and inconveniences of transportation in pioneer times.

The heavy freighting wagons, known as "prairie schooners," were used in connection with overland transportation to all points west of San Antonio. They were constructed to withstand the wear and tear of rocky and mountainous roads in western Texas and New Mexico, and they could be used elsewhere on account of their weight — about four thousand pounds.

The hind wheels measured five feet ten inches in height, and the [iron] tire was six inches wide and one inch thick. The front wheels were like them but were twelve inches lower. The axles were of solid iron, with spindles three inches in diameter, and the running gear was built for hard service. The wagon bed was twenty-four feet long and four and a half feet wide, and the sides were five and a half feet high. Wagon bows were attached to

each, and over them two heavy tarpaulins were
stretched, that protected the freight. On these
covers the owner's name was painted. The wood-
work of these wagons was painted deep blue and
the iron-work black.

Every wagon was furnished with a powerful
brake. The beam that constituted the brake was
six by eight inches and was made of choice hickory
timber. It was placed beneath the wagon box, and
a block of wood was fastened near each end, which
pressed against the wheels when the lever was
pulled by the driver.

An average load for such wagons was about seven thousand pounds. With ten small mules, sixteen bales of cotton could be transported. Bulky freight made the wagon sway from side to side when passing over rough roads, consequently it lightened the draft on the team. But it was dangerous to pass along sloping roads high up on the sides of mountains. It was necessary then to attach ropes to the two axles on the lower side, after which they were held by a dozen men moving along the slope above, to keep the wagon from toppling over into a gorge. There were many such places between San Antonio and El Paso.

The mules were small but active, with untiring energy and a constitution that enabled them to endure extreme hardships. The manner in which the ten [mules] were hitched brought them close to the load and made them almost a unit when a steady pull was necessary.

The prairie schooners encouraged San Antonio to extend her business connections with Mexico, and they did much toward [promoting] trade between the two countries and Europe. They opened a way for railroads that followed in their trail. Because they were the main dependence in the west for the transportation of goods, they were always insured a warm welcome. A long train of prairie schooners was attractive, and they were always picturesque.

The scarcity of water and grass on the route made it necessary for me to divide my daily journeys into three drives or camps, especially where the watering places were about fifty miles apart. Generally, when making a drive from one watering place to the next, we started about one o'clock in the afternoon. We drove until about six, when we stopped to eat supper and graze the teams. We started again at ten P.M. and drove until three A.M. when we camped without water. At seven we were under way again, and at ten we arrived at the watering place. There the teams were watered and turned loose to graze for about four hours, then were watered again before being hitched. Sometimes, when the distance between watering places was less than thirty miles, only one drive was made that day.

The inconveniences on account of a scarcity of water could not compare to the discomforts of protecting my mules and ourselves against the Indians. Knowing that they were constantly watching for an opportunity to overpower us, we were compelled to be alert at all times. When in camp at noon, while the herd was grazing in charge of a chief herdsman and his assistants, two teamsters stood guard on a prominent elevation nearby.

Arms used in my train were short guns of fifty caliber. The gun was carried in a scabbard fastened to the driver's saddle mule, and in camp was placed against the left wheel of his wagon. The forty-five caliber six shooter was carried in a scabbard in his cartridge belt, or was always in reach of his hands. The belt carried fifty rounds of cartridges for the needle gun and twelve rounds for the pistol. The guns ranged about eight thousand feet and the pistols about one thousand feet.

When we camped at night in a region infested by Indians, a detail of four men stood guard over the animals and were relieved every two hours. On such occasions the caporal,[1] wagon master, and all the teamsters slept in a group near the train, with their arms ready for use at a moment's notice.

My wagon train averaged about twelve wagons, and twenty-three men was the average number that accompanied it, including drivers and others. The herd consisted of about one hundred and fifty animals.

Mexicans made the most expert drivers. The most remarkable thing was the ease with which they picked out their teams on the darkest nights. They rarely made a mistake. It took about forty minutes to hitch up at night, or thirty minutes in the daytime. I seldom found one that was not reliable, and they were always ready, day or night, to attend to any duty that was required of them.

Every wagon train was under the general supervision of a wagon master, who was responsible for its management at all times, and directed its movements on a journey. The next important person was the caporal, who was in charge of the extra mules when moving and of all animals after

[1]caporal (Spanish) is the man in charge of the horses or mules.

making camp. He looked out for watering places and good grass and saw that the mules were not mistreated by the drivers.

A train, say of twelve wagons, was divided into two sections, and each section of six wagons was in charge of a captain. He was accountable for certain duties and for the placing of his wagons when forming a corral. The captains generally were expert drivers who understood their business.

The captain of the first section drove wagon No. 1, in the lead the first day's journey, and the captain of the second section led the following day. These changes in positions were necessary on a long journey, otherwise the teams in the rear sections would have been strained too much, on account of frequent stops, if they had traveled continuously in the same order.

The corral was important when the train consisted of a number of wagons, because it was necessary to the safety of the animals wherever the train was encamped. It served also as a fort which gave protection for man and beast when attacked by Indians or other enemies.

The mules were taken from the wagons and unharnessed. When turned loose they passed into the corral, where they were fed in long canvas troughs. From there they were driven in a herd through one of the large openings to a watering place or to pasture.

After the mules were returned to the enclosure,

the caporal cracked his whip and ordered the mules to take their places. They were then bridled, the ropes were removed, and every mule walked through the gap nearest the wagon to which he belonged. A company of soldiers could not have moved more orderly to their places.

Sometimes we were caught out in awful blizzards, and many times I was alone with my wagons, while the men were in neighboring cedar brakes with the mules. They had driven them there for protection during such weather.

On one of my trips from Chihuahua (chē wä′ wä) when I crossed the Pecos River at the

Horsehead Crossing, the ground was covered for days where buffalo had eaten off the small limbs from the trees as far as they could reach. Once a long train of wagons that was in charge of Captain Edgar, of San Antonio, was exposed to one of such blizzards, and he lost about sixty mules. They had bunched together for protection against the cold but were frozen to death. The place was known for many years as "Edgar's bone-yard."

— *August Santleben*

Things to Do

1. This is a true story about the "prairie schooners." Re-read the story to help you do the following:
   a. Why were the "prairie schooners" especially suitable for overland freighting?
   b. Where did the writer of this story operate freight caravans?
   c. Read aloud the description of a "schooner."
   d. Why was it dangerous for these wagons to pass over mountainous roads?
   e. Make an illustration of a train of prairie schooners.
   f. Describe how the daily journey was divided into three "drives."
   g. How were the trains protected against Indians?
   h. Why did Mexicans make excellent drivers?
   i. What were the duties of the wagon master, the caporal, and captains?
   j. How was a corral made from the wagons?
   k. How were the trains protected in blizzards?
2. Compare the dangers of transporting goods by prairie schooners with modern ways of transportation.

Crush, Texas

Texas once had a place that was a city for a single day. It had a population of about thirty thousand; and it had a jail, officers of the law, saloons, and cafes. Especially prominent were its magicians, snake charmers, fat ladies, flying jennies, and other entertainment features. Most important of all was its train wreck!

The town was named Crush, and it was on the Missouri, Kansas, and Texas Railroad between Hillsboro and Waco. It began its life on the morning of September 5, 1896, and ended it with the going down of the sun on that same day.

The idea of its founders was to have a real head-on collision between two trains, for the benefit of the public. There had been several wrecks shortly before that time, and they had attracted much attention. The railroad managers thought a wreck carefully planned and announced in advance would arouse even more interest.

And if it did, the company should make a profit by having excursion trains run to the scene. The officials wanted to avoid any deaths, but they wanted it to be a real collision. Excursions were popular in those days, and this one should be the most popular of all.

Such, at least, was the belief of W. G. Crush, General Passenger Agent of the railroad. It was rumored that some of the other officials were afraid of the scheme, but it seems that he finally convinced them that it was a good idea.

The place selected for the event was a tract of one hundred acres, many miles from any town. On the spot was a railroad spur, and there were several miles of double track and sidings. It was far enough from the largest cities to make excursion trains necessary and to give everyone plenty of room.

By sunrise the crowds were gathering — on horseback, in wagons and buggies, and on trains. Ice water was provided free, and other drinks might be had for money. One train pulled in after another, until there were thirty of them, and the place was a seething mass of people. It was presidential election year, and both the Democrats and the Republicans had speakers present.

At 4:30 P.M. the "trial heat" was run, for the sponsors wanted the trains to meet at a certain place, where the crowd could see the collision well. A couple of hundred-ton locomotives, exactly alike, were used, and to each engine six old freight cars were connected. Every care was taken to be perfectly fair and give both "contestants" equal chances.

Experienced men were chosen to run the engines, and the collision point was carefully roped off, to keep spectators from being hurt. The first engine backed about a mile and ran by at full speed. Then it backed up and the second engine had its run. Both made their runs in exactly the same time, which meant they should collide at the right place. After the trial runs the two trains slowly pulled up to the point chosen for the wreck, blew their whistles, and were photographed. Then they backed up exactly one mile in each direction.

The final signal was now given. The engineers answered with two short toots and pulled their throttles wide open. The engineers and firemen then swung from the cabs to the ground, leaving their charges to make the run without further human aid.

The giant locomotives hit each other like two angry monsters fighting a life and death battle. They reared up in front as if each one was trying to climb on top of the other. Their boilers burst,

sending hissing steam in every direction. There
was a dull thud when they met that reminded old
Confederate veterans of the firing of Civil War
cannon, and there were hideous noises as steel plates
and freight cars were torn apart or crushed.

The twelve freight cars were torn up so badly
that little was left of them but small pieces, scattered
up and down the railroad tracks for half a mile. In
some places wreckage was piled up in the ditches
near the tracks; and pieces of twisted steel, bolts,
and wood splinters went flying in every direction.

Officers of the law were unable to hold back

the crowd after the wreck; they broke through the ropes and swarmed over the place. Later it was learned that two people had been killed. One man, who had climbed into a tree near the track for a better view, was struck by a piece of flying iron, and a lady had her skull crushed by a length of chain. A photographer was hit in his left eye by an iron bolt, but he kept on making pictures. Others were injured in the scramble of the mob. The railroad became the defendant in several law suits that must have taken away most of their excursion profits.

For hours after the wreck, souvenir hunters took complete charge, grabbing everything that could be carried off as remembrances of the event. In many Texas homes gray-haired hosts later showed visitors a rusted bolt, a twisted bit of steel, or a burnt bit of wood. Then would come the story of the wildest train wreck they had ever seen. They never wanted to see another, they might say, but they would not have missed that one for any amount of money.

— *J. A. Rickard*

Things to Do

1. Discuss the plan of the early Texas railroad managers for making money by excursion trains.
2. Read the story aloud.
3. Do you think that people today would plan an event for pleasure or making money in which others might be injured? Think hard. Are you sure?

Then and Now

A Three Million-Acre House

The value of houses is usually figured in money, but in Texas there is a house whose value is measured in land. It was traded for a three million-acre ranch, (or for the lands that composed the ranch). The house is the state capitol at Austin, and the ranch was the old XIT, for years the largest in the world.

It all goes back to 1881, when the old capitol of Texas was burned to the ground, with little or nothing saved. Precious records were lost and the legislature, the governor, and other state officials had no place to do business. The loss of the building was not a great one, for it had long since become too small for the needs of the state, and there was a little insurance on it. But the state was not able to pay for a new building. The horrors of the Civil War and the waste of the Reconstruction government in Texas were still fresh in people's minds. They looked with suspicion on large spending of money. The depression and the hard times of the seventies were even fresher in their memories. The state treasury was empty, taxes were low, and the people were opposed to raising them. Indeed, so scarce was money that not much would be secured if taxes *were* raised.

Old State Capitol Built 1853.

But the state had plenty of one resource--land. When it entered the Union in 1845, the agreement was that the new state would keep its public lands. Although it had made huge gifts of these lands to the public schools, the State University, A. & M. College, each of the counties, the railroads, and many of its war veterans, it still had some fifty million acres left.

With so little money and so much land, the legislature did a natural thing — it decided to use about three million acres for building a capitol. To be sure they would know what they were doing, a committee of the legislature had architects draw up a complete plan, which the lawmakers approved. The capitol was to be of pink granite from quarries in nearby Burnet County. The completed structure was to be 308 feet high, 528 feet long, and 290 feet at its greatest width. It was to be situated on the same choice location as the old capitol — on a hill commanding a view of present-day Congress Avenue in Austin.

There were some who said that no bidders would be found, for land was cheap, and cutting and hauling such enormous granite rocks would be expensive. Indeed, it was some time before any interest was shown beyond mild questioning. Texas builders did not find the project attractive, nor were builders from other states interested in the plan.

Then, certain English and Scottish cattle raisers inquired about it. They wanted to locate a ranch in Texas, because of the report that cattle could be raised there very cheaply; and there was not only a heavy demand for cattle, but also a good price for them in Europe. Also, the perfection of the process of refrigeration or cold storage about that time made meat shipments from Texas to Europe possible.

A company of English and Scottish investors was formed, and it accepted the offer of the Texas legislature. The land the company received was located in a huge block on the Staked Plains of

Texas. There the owners established the XIT ranch. They hired Texas cowboys and foremen, spent huge sums on newly-invented barbed wire fences, bought cattle of all breeds wherever they could find them, and went into the cattle business on a grand scale. The name, as well as the brand, "XIT", was chosen because the letters stood for "Ten in Texas." The land holdings covered parts of ten Texas counties: Dallam, Hartley, Oldham, Deaf Smith, Parmer, Castro, Bailey, Lamb, Cochran, and Hockley.

The old XIT ranch was long the most prominent one in Texas. Finally, its owners yielded to the temptation of rising land values and falling cattle prices. They divided the huge ranch into smaller ones and sold them, making large profits. Several ranches, still large by ordinary standards, now appeared. The Littlefield Ranch was one of them.

Before many more years the settlers had entered the whole Plains area. Some ranches still survive, and a few old-time cowboys that once worked on the XIT are still living. But the country, as a whole, is now devoted to farming rather than ranching. Up-to-date farms, prosperous cities, and modern highways have replaced the herds of cattle which once roamed over the old XIT ranch lands.

The Texas capitol is still in good condition, all of its 500 rooms in daily use; but there is a signal on its dome which was not in its original planning

J. P. Crowe

The Capitol today.

— a warning to aviators. Texans appreciate the grandeur of their capitol building, and many thousands of visitors admire it each year.

— *J. A. Rickard*

Things to Do

1. With what did the legislature of Texas pay for its capitol, and how much?
2. Describe the building.
3. Why were the English and Scottish investors interested in securing Texas ranch lands?
4. Tell what the ranch was called and why.
5. Tell how the land is used today.
6. What new signal has been placed on the capitol dome?

Flag Song of Texas

O prairie breeze, blow sweet and pure,
    And Southern sun shine bright
To bless our flag, where'er may gleam
    Its single star of light;
But should the sky grow dark with wrath,
    The tempest burst and rave,
It still shall float undauntedly,
    The standard of the brave!

Flag of our State, O glorious flag!
    Unsullied in peace, and triumphant in war;
Heroes have fought for you,
Statesmen have wrought for you —
    Emblazoned in glory you bear the Lone Star!

By deeds of arms our land was freed,
    And priceless the reward!
Brave Milam died and Fannin fell
    Its sacred rights to guard;
Our patriot force with mighty will
    Triumphant set it free,
And Travis, Bowie, Crockett gave
    Their lives for liberty!

And when on San Jacinto's plain
    The Texians heard the cry,
"Remember, men, the Alamo!"
    They swore to win or die;

Resistless in their high resolve,
　　They forced the foe to yield,
And freedom crowned their victory
　　On that illustrious field!

O Texas, tell the story o'er,
　　With pride recall each name,
And teach your sons to emulate
　　Their virtues and their fame;
So shall your grandeur still increase,
　　Your glory shine afar,
For deathless honor guards the flag
　　Where gleams the proud Lone Star!
　　　　　　　　— *Mrs. Lee C. Harby*

The River of Many Names

Early explorers along the Gulf Coast, seeing a grove of palm trees at its mouth, called it the River of Palms. Other overland explorers, farther up the stream, called it the River of May. Still others named it the Rio Bravo and the River of the North, but we know it as the Rio Grande.

It rises in the Rocky Mountains. After a sixteen hundred mile trip, most of which forms the Texas-Mexico boundary, the river grows tired and deposits its load of sediment, or settlings, along its banks before flowing into the Gulf of Mexico.

Thus developed the Lower Rio Grande Valley, a region famous for citrus fruits, winter vegetables, cotton, and other crops. In fertility this valley has been compared with that of the Nile River of Egypt. Indeed, it is like that area in another respect — its dependence on river water for irrigation, without which the country is too dry and too hot to grow plentiful crops year after year. With water, almost anything can be raised.

But Mexico also has an interest in the Rio Grande; in fact, the middle of the river is the boundary line between Mexico and the United States. The constantly changing bed of the stream has complicated the problem at times, for sometimes, due to

Marker on Rio Grande between Texas and Mexico

floods, a piece of land will be in the United States on one day and in Mexico the next.

The use of the river water, however, is the biggest problem presented. On the Texas side the main tributaries of the Rio Grande are the Pecos, the Devil's River, and other smaller streams. On the Mexican side are the Conchos, Salado, and San Juan.

Near its source the Rio Grande is fed by springs and mountain streams; but much of this water is caught in the Elephant Butte dam in New Mexico, and is used for irrigation in Southern New Mexico, Western Texas, and Northwestern Mexico.

The Pecos River, on the northern side, furnishes much water, but most of that which reaches the Lower Valley comes from the Mexican rivers.

In recent years, however, Mexico has developed irrigation projects of her own and has insisted on a more equal division of the river waters. The situation has been further complicated by the Colorado River problem. This far-western stream flows south between California and Arizona and into Mexico; but when it reaches Mexico not much of the water is left, for it has been used in the United States. Naturally, Mexico has insisted that both problems be settled at the same time.

Seasonal rains have also complicated matters. Often the lower portions of the Rio Grande have been at flood stage. During such periods enough water flows into the Gulf of Mexico to water an area many times the size of the Lower Rio Grande Valley, if it could be caught in reservoirs or turned into channels north or south of the river. There have been times, especially during the hot summer months, when the river bed was almost dry — at the season when irrigated crops needed water most.

Floods higher up the river, or on its tributaries, have destroyed much property, ruined crops, and even caused loss of life. The newly erected Falcon Dam prevented such a disaster in the Lower Valley shortly after it was built, but farther up stream the damage was great.

Drainage problems in the Lower Valley, near

the coast, have also been troublesome. Underground water from the Gulf of Mexico is so close to the surface that the region near the Gulf sometimes becomes water-soaked. This condition reduces the yield of citrus fruit and other crops.

The solution to this problem has been drainage ditches. A valley-wide drainage system was planned by experts, from engineering plans calling for the construction of three large storage dams. The planners had to wait until the Treaty of 1945 could be ratified before they could be built. That time finally arrived, and on October 19, 1953, the giant Falcon Dam was formally dedicated. Other dams farther upstream have been planned.

The whole question of the use of Rio Grande water is bound up in a series of treaties between the United States and Mexico, beginning in 1848. The final treaty of 1945 calls for a fair division of the waters of the Rio Grande, the Colorado, and the Tiajuana Rivers, and makes it possible for water to be drained out of these streams into canals far out into the country. This provides for irrigating land which in the past did not receive any water. The dams, of which Falcon is the first, will catch water during flood time to be released gradually during dry seasons.

In this treaty Mexico was guaranteed 1,500,000 acre feet annually from the Colorado River, an "acre foot" being the amount of water that covers one acre to the depth of one foot. On the Rio Grande

Rio Grande and Mexican Power Plant

below Fort Quitman, the river water is being divided equally.

Thus is the river of many names being harnessed, and new gardens of Eden or Nile Valleys are being brought into existence.

— *J. A. Rickard*

Things to Do

1. On a map of the United States, locate the Rio Grande and its tributaries.
2. Locate the Elephant Butte Dam in New Mexico. How does this dam affect the Lower Rio Grande Valley?
3. Why were the people of Mexico concerned with the Colorado River problem?
4. How do seasonal rains affect the Rio Grande?
5. What is the purpose of the huge Falcon Dam?

Wild Life on Padre Island

On the Texas Gulf Coast is a long, narrow "treasure island," extending from Corpus Christi to Point Isabel. It is known today as Padre Island, but for thousands of years it was unnamed and uninhabited, except by wild animals, birds, and Indians. Later, pirates, adventurers, and shipwrecked sailors found it a quiet, sunswept refuge. Now, Texans and others have discovered Padre Island, and Laguna Madre, the narrow, shallow water that for nearly one hundred and thirty miles separates the island from the Texas mainland.

Both are now open to the public, one road having been built across to Padre from Corpus Christi and another from Port Isabel to the southern end of the island. More than ten million dollars was spent building these causeways, and much more will be spent in the near future in erecting facilities on the island for visitors. Already more than a million automobiles have crossed the Corpus Christi causeway, and the Port Isabel road seems to be just as crowded.

The reason for this popularity is not hard to find, for nature has made the island attractive. Along the Gulf side are more than a hundred miles of excellent bathing and fishing beaches. Automobiles can travel over much of the distance near the

Highway on Padre Island

water, and paved highways are gradually being built.

In the Gulf one can catch mackerel, tarpon, sailfish, redfish, and many other kinds. If he prefers the quieter waters of the Laguna, he may catch trout, golden croakers, drum, or perhaps flounders — and some of these are found in both places. He can fish by wading, by boat, or from piers; and along the intracoastal canal, running the length of the island and farther, fishing is good most of the time.

Padre Island has attractions also for bird lovers and other naturalists. Geologists have classified at least eighteen varieties of sea shells, and examples of most of them can be found. There are some jack rabbits, coyotes, and rattlesnakes; and there are many kinds of sea birds. Sea gulls find the beach after tide a good place to eat for it brings in bits of vegetable matter, small fish, and other tidbits. At night, after high tides have swept the shore clean, the gulls leave for the sand dunes, of which the island has many. Patches of scrub oaks around these dunes are the homes of the great blue herons. They build their nests in the top limbs, leaving the lower limbs for blackbirds.

There are more than a hundred kinds of birds in the region. Some, like the plover, the tern, and the willet, are primarily land birds; but more are water fowls. Ducks are well represented, of various species and kinds, and flights of ten thousand in one group are not unknown.

Then there are the laughing gulls, with their black heads and begging ways. They hover over camps, squawking loudly and expertly catching any food that may be thrown into the air. Snowy and reddish egrets and Louisiana herons are likewise seen. With the exception of the heron, probably the largest bird around the island is the brown pelican. He is an expert fisher. When he dives from a great height into the water, watchers can be pretty sure that he has a fish.

Birds and cactus on the Island

Near the inner edges of Padre, on the Laguna side, are several smaller islands that are favorite places for the breeding of birds. People who visit them during the hatching season report that they contain so many nests, eggs, and young birds that one can hardly step without crushing one or the other.

The island is rich in history and legend. It was early inhabited by the fierce Karankaway Indians and for a long time a possession of Spain. It was a Spanish priest, José Nicolás Ballí (hō sä´ nē kō läs´ bä yē´) who made the first white settlement there. This gave the island its name. In 1804, with a grant from the Spanish King in his hand, he established a mission with a ranch attached, calling it the Rancho de la Santa Cruz. He did not convert many Indians, but he remained on the island for several years.

Meanwhile, in 1821, Mexico had become independent of Spain, and five years later Ballí secured from the new government a grant to the whole of Padre. It was from his heirs that later purchases were made, until a number of people owned parts of the island.

Afterward, in the nineteenth century, several other groups visited the island, one of them being John V. Singer, brother of the inventor of the sewing machine of that name. Shipwrecked there in 1847, he and his family remained until the latter days of the War between the States, or about 1865. He rebuilt the Santa Cruz Ranch and established a colony.

The best-known island resident was Pat Dunn, who as "Duke of Padre" occupied the region from 1879 to 1937. For him it was an ideal cattle ranch. There was plenty of grass; no fences were needed; cattle stealing was almost impossible on account of surrounding water; and there were no troublesome neighbors. He built ranch houses and corrals of driftwood. He had Louisiana pine plank shacks,

South American mahogany fence posts, wine barrel tables, door hinges from wrecked steamers, and a wash basin made of a cask with Japanese lettering. Later, the Jones Brothers of Kansas City became the main owners, but the King Ranch owns six thousand acres of the land on Padre.

Many blood and treasure stories are linked with the island. For a long time it was the stopping place of smugglers, pirates, and other outlaws. Many coins with strange inscriptions have been uncovered, and in 1904 the Gulf waters washed up chests filled with more than a million dollars worth of gold.

Such, at least, is the story, and there are other

The beach

ones to match it. Another yarn has it that a man named Mercer, while walking along the beach one day, kicked over a tobacco can and kept going. Another man behind him picked up the rusted can and found in it three hundred dollars in gold.

John Singer — so they say — found $80,000 in treasure and buried it six miles from his Santa Cruz Ranch headquarters. But so soon did the sand cover the place that neither he nor his son could find the treasure again. It is still there, waiting to be found.

When Cortés conquered Mexico — so they say again — he sent out twenty ships loaded with gold, silver, and gems taken from the Aztec Indians. A hurricane struck. Sixteen of the ships were stranded and wrecked on Padre. Only one ever reached Spain. A salvage crew, sent to search for them, found all but one. That one is still somewhere beneath the sands of the island. In 1904 — says the story — a man named Meuly found the lone ship, with a cargo of a million dollars, and buried it, planning to return later. But sand also buried his markings, and that loot, too, is waiting to be found. He is supposed to have found the ship about thirty-five miles south of Corpus Christi Pass, which is at the northern end of Padre.

Several wrecked ships have found their last resting place along the Gulf side of the island. One of these, the *Merrimac*, a tugboat laden with salvaged ammunition and supplies from a sinking vessel during the 1915 trouble with Mexico, ran ashore on Padre. For many years it withstood sand and tide, but recent visitors to the spot were unable to locate it.

Another ship, the *Mary Jane*, showed prominently on the beach some years ago, but beachcombers carried off what the sand had not covered. Nowadays salvage operations keep the beaches pretty well cleared, but now and then shortly after a storm one can discover the last remains of a sea tragedy.

Courtesy of State Highway Department

A sea tragedy

About the center of Padre's length is a bend called Devil's Elbow, the graveyard of several ships. Hurricanes have visited the region many times: there was one in 1916 and another in 1933. Ships finding themselves in trouble with the elements generally landed in Devil's Elbow — but sometimes they were wrecked. The *Nicaragua*, still showing in part, is one of these.

The coming of tourists is changing things. In a few years Padre Island may be mostly highways, beach resorts, and other signs of civilization. But not everything will be changed. The long shore line, the wind, the waves, the sand, and — it is hoped — some of the fish — these will be there. The work of many years cannot be erased suddenly. Future generations will enjoy it.

— *J. A. Rickard*

Courtesy of McGregor Studios

Sand dunes

Things to Do

1. On a map of Texas, locate Padre Island and Laguna Madre.
2. Why has much money been spent in building causeways to this island?
3. Why is the island of great interest to naturalists and geologists?
4. Discuss its history. Get your facts from the story.
5. Who was the "Duke of Padre"? Why is his home famous?
6. Have you tried writing a lost treasure, sea, or pirate story? Take the facts that are mentioned in the story about one of the following and use them as your plot:
   a. Cortés.
   b. Padre Ballí.
   c. Mercer.
   d. John Singer.
   e. Meuly.
   f. The wrecked ships, the *Merrimac*, the *Mary Jane*, the *Nicaragua*.
   g. Devil's Elbow.
7. When you have finished and shared your stories, you might enjoy having your teacher read aloud Stevenson's *Treasure Island*.

La Villita

La Villita

In the heart of the business district of old San Antonio is an area occupying more than a block square that is older than most of the city. It has been restored at great expense, to present a true picture of colonial and pioneer life.

Called "La Villita," (lä vē yĕ′ tä) the Spanish term for Little Village, it is a place of adobe houses, hand-carved mesquite doors, flower-bordered ponds, water ditches, shady patios, deeply recessed windows, shake shingle roofs, rough flagstone walks, and worn-stone doorsteps. For two centuries it actually existed, only to lose its identity when a big city grew up around it. With the aid of the Carnegie Foundation, the city of San Antonio, and the National Youth Administration employing 1800 people, it has been rebuilt.

Its origin goes back to the days of the early eighteenth century. When the missions were founded at that time, there were two San Antonio settlements. One was the mission settlement itself, inhabited largely by Franciscan Fathers and Indians. The other was the Presidio, or fort, of San Fernando de Bexar, which was the barracks and camps for soldiers protecting those missions.

In a short while there was a need for a third settlement. The place was attracting tradesmen, camp followers, adventurers, and others who were not connected with either the missions or the fort. The settlement of La Villita met this need. Families of some soldiers lived there also.

It was on the site of an old Indian village, on the east side of the San Antonio River, which separated the place from the more aristocratic Villa of San Fernando. In the course of time the missions declined, and some of the mission families and soldiers of the Presidio began to live there. Then a flood covered the San Fernando region, almost washing it away, and some of the survivors went to La Villita, where the ground was higher.

Finally, in the nineteenth century, came the Americanos (ä mä rē cä′ nŏs) to the village. Deaf Smith was there in 1819; Moses Austin and the Baron de Bastrop came in 1820, and James Bowie went there in 1828. As the Texas Revolution drew near, a Mexican army was camped nearby, and its leader, General Cos, had his home there.

After the fall of the Alamo and the independence of Texas, still other Americanos appeared. Captain Jack Hays made La Villita his headquarters, while he headed the Texas Rangers and conquered the Indians. Samuel A. and Mary A. Maverick moved in and identified themselves with San Antonio. Germans entered, making new buildings and bringing their customs and foods. The Poles and the French selected the place for homes also.

When war between the states was declared, many of the men left the Little Village, to serve in the army, but otherwise life there was much the same. The twentieth century came, and San Antonio grew into a large city. It was a fitting time for the sleepy old village to be reborn, and in 1939 this rebirth occurred. Late in December, 1939, the Carnegie Corporation made a Christmas gift to La Villita. With a $15,000 grant, and N.Y.A. aid, the city of San Antonio began the erection of a large building called Bolívar Building in honor of the South American patriot. It now houses a Spanish American library and museum and is used as a community center for the city of San Antonio.

Other features of the reconstructed village shortly appeared. Because the place was intended as one where Latin American culture might find a home, the main Plaza was called Juárez Plaza, in honor of Benito Juárez, who had led Mexico in the overthrow of the Austrian Maximilian, Emperor of Mexico. The little street running through the village was renamed King Philip V Street, after the Spanish King who had ruled when Villita was first settled.

Other old landmarks, or old original houses, were restored. Today the visitor can see the old Cos house, the Caxias house, and five others from the long ago, rebuilt as they once stood.

One prominent feature of the restored village is the arts and crafts program which is carried on there. It includes classes in woodworking, metal working, pottery, leather-tooling, weaving, and other crafts. The products of these classes are sold to tourists and other visitors. In one year recently, artists and crafstmen taught several thousand apprentices in fifteen shops.

La Villita also serves as a community center for social activities. In one year nearly five hundred club and social functions were scheduled, and as many as a hundred thousand guests visited the place.

Indeed, La Villita has an unusual attraction for visitors and tourists, for it gives one an accurate picture of life as it existed a century or more ago — at least so far as buildings are concerned. There they find a place of quietness and simplicity, a reminder of a way of life long gone, but one that should be remembered.

A quaint old Spanish village this — in the heart of a romantic city.

— *J. A. Rickard*

Things to Do

1. Discuss the story, using these questions:
   a. Where is La Villita in San Antonio?
   b. Why did the people want to restore it?
   c. Why were there two settlements in San Antonio in the early eighteenth century?
   d. Who were some of the famous persons who lived in the village?
   e. Describe La Villita as it is today.
2. Why is the restoration of early villages, buildings, etc., important to us today?
3. When you are in San Antonio, try to visit La Villita.

Glossary

Glossary

Guide to Pronunciation, see page 329

A.

a-bode' (à-bōd'). Dwelling

ab'o-rig'i-nal (ăb'ŏ-rĭj'ĭ-năl). First; original

a-breast' (à-brĕst'). Side by side

ac-count'a-ble (ă-koun'tà-b'l). Responsible

ac-cu'mu-la'ting (ă-kū'mū-lā-tĭng). Gathering; piling up

ac'cu-rate (ăk'ŭ-rĭt). Exact; correct

ad-ja'cent (ă-jā'sĕnt). Bordering

ad'vent (ăd'vĕnt). Any coming; arrival

af-fect' (ă-fĕkt'). Influence

a-light'ed (à-lī'tĕd). Got down; dismounted

am'bush (ăm'bŏŏsh). To hide for the purpose of attacking an enemy by surprise

a-miss' (à-mĭs'). Improper

an'es-thet'ic (ăn'ĕs-thĕt'ĭk). An agent that causes entire or partial loss of feeling or sensation

an'i-mat'ed (ăn'ĭ-māt'ĕd). Lively; full of spirit

an'nex-a'tion (ă'-nĕks-ā'shŭn). Attaching; uniting one thing to another

an'nu-al-ly (ăn'ŭ-ăl-lĭ). Once a year

an'te-room' (ăn'tê-rōōm'). A room before, or forming an entrance, to another

ap-par'ent (ăp-păr'ĕnt). Clear to the understanding; plain; evident

ap-pren'tices (ă-prĕn'tĭ-sĕs). Those bound by legal agreement to serve another for a certain time to learn an art or trade

ar'id (ăr'ĭd). Without moisture; dry; barren

ar'my post' (är'mĭ pōst'). The place at which soldiers are stationed

ar-rest'or (à-rĕst'ẽr). A device for stopping something

ar-roy'o (ă-roi'ō). Spanish name for a small stream or its dry bed

as-sas'sin (ă-săs'ĭn). One who kills by surprise or in secret

as-ser'tive (ă-sûr'tĭv). Aggressive; positive

a-stray' (à-strā'). Out of the right way

at-tend'ant (ă-tĕn'dănt). Escort; one who attends

aus'pi-ces (ôs'pĭ-sĕz). Protection; patronage and care

a-venge' (à-vĕnj'). To get satisfaction for

B.

beach'comb'er (bēch'kōm'ẽr). A loafer who lives along the seacoast

bel'fry (bĕl'frĭ). The separate or attached bell tower of a church

bid'der (bĭd'ẽr). One who offers a price for payment

breach (brēch). A breaking of a trust or obligation

breast'works' (brĕst'wûrks'). Fort

Glossary

C.

cache (kăsh). To hide, usually in a hole in the ground

cal'cu-la'tions (kăl'kŭ-lā'-shŭns). Reckoning; forecast

cal'i-ber (kăl'ĭ-bẽr). The diameter of the bore of a gun

ca-pac'i-ty (kȧ-păs'ĭ-tĭ). Capability

ca'per (kā'pẽr). A skip; a jump, as in mirth or dancing

cap-o-ral' (kăp-ȯ-răl'). Spanish word for wagon master

car'bine (kär'bīn). A short light rifle

car'go (kär'gō). Load; freight

cask (kȧsk). A barrel-shaped vessel made of staves, headings and hoops, usually for liquids

cas-sa'va (kă-sä'vä). A tropical plant which has fleshy edible roots that provide a nutritious starch

cast'a-way (kȧst'ȧ-wā). A shipwrecked person

cause'way (kôz'wā). A raised highway over water or wet ground

cav'a-liers (kăv'ȧ-lērs). One of the court party in England

cav'al-ry (kăv'ăl-rĭ). That part of a military force which serves on horseback

cen'tu-ries (sĕn'tū-rĭz). Periods of a hundred years

chute (shōōt). An inclined plane or trough, down which something may be made to pass

clus'tered (klŭs'tẽrd). Grown together in a bunch

com'man-dant' (kom'ăn-dänt'). A commanding officer

com-plai'sant (kŏm-plā'zănt). Courteous; obliging

com'pli-cate (kŏm'plĭ-kāt). To make difficult, intricate

com-plied' (kŏm-plīd'). Yielded; consented

con-fi'ded (kŏn-fī'dĕd). Told in confidence

con'sti-tu'tion (kŏn'stĭ-tū'-shŭn). All of the physical and vital powers of a person

con-tempt' (kŏn-tĕmpt'). State of being despised

con-tin'u-ous (kŏn-tĭn'ŭ-ŭs). Having continuity of parts; without stopping

con'tra-band (kŏn'trȧ-bănd). Smuggled goods

con-trac'tor (kŏn-trăk'tẽr). One who agrees to do work or supply materials

con-vinc'ing (kŏn-vĭn'sĭng). Satisfying or assuring by proof

cord'wood (kôrd'wŏŏd). Wood piled up or sold in cords

cor'po-rate (kôr'pȯ-rĭt). Formed into a body by legal act

cor'sair (kôr'sâr). Pirate

coun'te-nance (koun'tê-năns). Face

cour'i-er (kŏŏr'ĭẽr). A special messenger

cra-vat (krȧ-văt'). A necktie

cri-sis (krī'sĭs). A crucial time

cul'prit (kŭl'prĭt). One guilty of a crime.

cur'a-tive (kūr'ȧ-tĭv). Used in the cure of diseases

Glossary

cus'to-dy (kŭs'tô-dĭ). A keeping or guarding

cus'tom-ar'y (kŭs'tŭm-ĕr'ĭ). Agreeing with, or according to custom

D.

de-ceived (dê-sēvd'). Tricked; misled

de-creed' (dê-krēd'). To command; ordered

def'i-cit (dĕf'ĭ-sĭt). Deficiency in amount, as of income

deg'ra-da'tion (dĕg'rà-dā'-shŭn). Disgrace; shame

de-ject'ed (dê-jĕk'tĕd). Depressed

de-lib'er-ate-ly (dê-lĭb'ĕr-ĭt-lĭ). Slow in action; not hurried

del'i-ca-cy (dĕl'ĭ-kà-sĭ). A luxury; very special

de-pres'sion (dê-prĕsh'ŭn). A period in which trade is reduced in amount

de-scent' (dê-sĕnt'). Ancestry

des'o-la'tion (dĕs'-ô-lā-shŭn). Ruin

des'ti-na'tion (dĕs'tĭ-nā'shŭn). The place set for the end of a journey

des'ti-ny (dĕs'tĭ-nĭ). Lot; fate

des'ti-tute (dĕs'-ti-tūt). In a condition of extreme want

de-vour' (dê-vour'). To eat up greedily or ravenously

de-vout' (dê-vout'). A solemn or reverent attitude toward religious observances

dis-charge' (dĭs-chärj'). Release

dis-cre'tion (dĭs-krĕsh'ŭn). Power of free decision; individual judgment

dis-may' (dĭs-mā'). Sudden loss of spirit through fear

dis-patched' (dĭs-păchd'). Sent off or away, especially on official business

dis-place' (dĭs-plās'). To take the place of

doc'ile (dŏs'ĭl). Gentle

dou'blet (dŭb'lĕt). A close fitting, often elaborate jacket, worn by men in Western Europe in the Renaissance

E.

e'co-nom'ic (ē'kô-nŏm'ĭk). Pertaining to the management of the affairs of a business

e'gret (ē'grĕt). Any of various herons which, during the breeding season, bear long plumes

el'e-va'tion (ĕl'ê-vā'shŭn). A raised place

em-bark' (ĕm-bärk'). To put or go on shipboard for a voyage

em'i-grant (ĕm'ĭ-grănt). Those who moved from one place of abode to another

em'pha-size (ĕm'fà-sīz). To stress

en'er-get'ic (ĕn'ĕr-jĕt'ĭk). Forceful; vigorous

en-treat'y (ĕn-trēt'ĭ). Request

e-quip'ping (ê-kwĭp'pĭng). Fitting out

es'cort (ĕs'kôrt). A group of soldiers accompanying another for protection

es-teem' (ĕs-tēm'). To set a value on; to appreciate

e-ven'tu-al-ly (ê-vĕn'tû-ăl-lĭ). Finally; ultimately

322

Glossary

ex-ag′ger-a′tion (ĕg-zăj′ēr-ā′-shŭn). Overstatement

ex-ces′sive (ĕk-sĕs′ĭv). More than is needed.

ex′pe-di′tion (ĕks′pė-dĭsh′ŭn). A journey for a specific purpose

ex′plo-ra′tion (ĕks′plȯ-rā′-shŭn). Discovery of land

ex-posed′ (ĕks-pōzd′). Unprotected, as from the weather

ex-ten′sive (ĕks-tĕn′sĭv). Broad; wide

ex′tri-cate (ĕks′trĭ-kāt). To free from difficulties; liberate

F.

fa-cade′ (fȧ-säd′). The face of a building

fa-cil′i-ty (fȧ-sĭl′ĭ-tĭ). A thing that promotes the ease of any action, operation, or course of conduct

faked (fākd). "Changed" in order to deceive

fan-tas′tic (făn-tăs′tĭk). Imaginary; unreal

fer-til′i-ty (fēr-tĭl′ĭ-tĭ). Being able to produce in abundance

fic-ti′tious (fĭk-tĭsh′ŭs). Imaginary

flanked (flăngkd). Placed at the side

foe (fō). Enemy

fol′ly (fŏl′ĭ). Lacking in sense; foolish

for-bid′ding (fŏr-bĭd′ĭng). Repelling approach

fore′cas-tle (fōr′kȧs′l). That part of the upper deck of a vessel forward of the mast

fore-run′ner (fōr-rŭn′ēr). One who goes ahead

for′ti-fi-ca′tion (fôr′tĭ-fĭ-kā′-shŭn). A fortified place or position

franc (frăngk). A coin in French money

free′boot′er (frē′bōōt′ēr). One who goes about plundering

fre′quent (frē′kwĕnt). Often

G.

gar′nished (gär′nĭsht). Decorated; adorned

gen′er-a′tion (jĕn′ēr-ā′shŭn). The ordinary period of time at which one rank follows another, or father is succeeded by child

gen-til′i-ty (jĕn-tĭl′ĭ-tĭ). Those who possess courage, dignity or courtesy

gig (gĭg). A light two-wheeled, one-horse carriage

gra′ding (grā′dĭng). To reduce to a level, or to an evenly progressive ascent, as a canal or a road

graph′ic (grăf′ĭk). Vividly described

griev′ances (grēv′ăn-sĕs). Sufferings; injustices; causes of uneasiness or complaint

guid′ance (gīd′ăns). Guiding; direction

gul′ly (gŭl′lĭ). A small valley or gorge dug out by running water, especially after rains

H.

haz′ard (hăz′ērd). Danger; risk

323

Glossary

her'e-tics (hĕr'ĕ-tĭks). Those who, having made a profession of Christian belief, reject the doctrine of their church

horse'whipped' (hôrs'hwipt'). Flogged with a whip for horses

hos'pi-ta-ble (hŏs'pĭ-tȧ-b'l). Receiving and entertaining guests generously and kindly

hos-til'i-ty (hŏs-tĭl'ĭ-tĭ). Being hostile or angry

I.

I'bis (ī'bĭs). Any of certain wading birds related to the heron

i-den'ti-ty (ī-dĕn'tĭ-tĭ). That which makes one different from others

in-ac'tion (ĭn-ăk'shŭn). Lack of action; idleness

in'ci-dent (ĭn'sĭ-dĭnt). An event, occurrence

in-cred'i-ble (ĭn-krĕd'ĭ-b'l). Too improbable to admit of belief

in'dis-pen'sa-ble (ĭn'dĭs-pĕn'-sȧ-b'l). Cannot do without

in-duced' (ĭn-dūst'). Moved by persuasion or influence

in-dus'tri-al (ĭn-dŭs'trĭ-ăl). Having to do with industry

in-fe'ri-or'i-ty (ĭn-fer'ĭ-ŏr'-ĭ-tĭ). An inferior person or thing; something of little or less importance

in-fes'ted (ĭn-fĕs'tĭd). Troubled greatly by number or presence

in-hab'it (ĭn-hăb'ĭt). To live in

in-laid' (ĭn-lād'). Set into a surface so as to form a decorative design

in-scrip'tion (ĭn-skrĭp'shŭn). Writing; an engraved record

in-sig'ni-a (ĭn-sĭg'nĭ-ȧ). Emblems

in-sta-bil'-i-ty (ĭn'stȧ-bĭl'ĭ-tĭ). Unsteadiness

in'ter-na'tion-al (ĭn'tĕr-năsh'-ŭn-ăl). Affecting two or more nations

in-ter'pret-ers (ĭn-tûr'prĕt-ĕrs). Those who explain or tell the meaning of

in'ter-val (ĭn'tĕr-văl). A space of time between any two points or events

in'tra-coas'tal (ĭn'trȧ-kōs'tăl). Within or on the inside of the coast

in-trust' (ĭn-trŭst'). To surrender something to another with confidence regarding his care of it

in-ves'tor (ĭn-vĕs'tĕr). One who lays out money in business with the view of obtaining an income or profit

J.

ja-ve-li'na (hä-vä-lē'nä). (from jabalina, Spanish). A Mexican wild hog

junc'tion (jŭnk'shŭn). The place or point of union

L.

land'marks' (lănd'märks'). Any conspicuous object on land that marks a place

Glossary

league (lēg). A measure of distance of about 3.45 miles

lib'er-al'i-ty (lĭb'ēr-ăl'ĭ-tĭ). Giving gifts generously

loin (loin). The front part of the hindquarter of an animal

lux-u'ri-ant (lŭks-ū'rĭ-ănt). Fertile; rich growth

M.

main'te-nance (mān'tė-nǎns). The upkeep of property

ma-raud'er (mȧ-rôd'ēr). One who raids or plunders

mav'er-ick (mǎv'ēr-ĭk). A motherless calf, claimed by the first one branding it

mer'it (mĕr'ĭt). To earn by service or performance; deserve

mi'grate (mī'grāt). To move from one place to another with the intention of setting up a home

mis'sile (mĭs'ĭl). Bullet

mor'sel (môr'sĕl). A small piece of food

mus'lin (mŭz'lĭn). Any of various coarser or heavier cotton goods

mus'ter (mŭs'tēr). Assemble; call together

mu'tu-al (mū'tů-ăl). Having the same relation to each other

myr'i-ad (mĭr'ĭ-ăd). A large number

N.

nar-rat'ed (nǎ-rāt'd). Told, as a story

nav'i-ga-ble (nǎv'ĭ-gȧ-b'l). Deep enough and wide enough to afford passage by vessels

nav'i-ga-tion (nǎv'ĭ-gā-shŭn). Act or art of managing a ship

neg'a-tive (nĕg'ȧ-tĭv). Not positive; against

neu'tral (nū'trǎl). Not engaged on either side

north'er-ly (nôr'thēr'lĭ). Directed toward the north

no'ta-ry (nō'tȧ-rĭ). Public officer who attests or certifies deeds and other writings to make them authentic

no'ti-fied (nō'tĭ-fīd). Gave notice of; told

no'ti-fy (nō'tĭ-fī). To make known

nub'bin (nŭb'ĭn). Any small or imperfect ear of Indian corn

O.

o-blig'ing (ȯ-blīj'ĭng). Agreeable; courteous

ob'sta-cle (ŏb'stȧ-k'l). That which stands in the way or opposes

oc'u-lar (ŏk'ů-lēr). Received by sight; visual

o'di-um (ō'dĭ-ŭm). Hatred

of-fi'ci-ate (ŏ-fĭsh'ĭ-āt). To act as an officer in performing a duty

or'a-tor (ŏr'ȧ-tēr). A public speaker

oust (oust). To turn out; expel

out'let (out'lĕt). A means or way of escape or entrance

Glossary

P.

pa'dre (pä'drĕ). Spanish word for monk or priest

pal'i-sade (păl'ĭ-sād). A fence of poles or stakes for defense

par (pär). Equal in value

pass'port (pȧs'pōrt). A document which secures admission or acceptance

peas'ant-ry (pĕz'ănt-rĭ). Peasants; a group of people who are peasants

per'ish-a-ble (pĕr'ĭsh-ȧ-b'l). Subject to destruction or deterioration.

pic'tur-esque (pĭk'tŭr-esk). Like a picture in coloring, design, technique or the like

pil'grim-age (pĭl'grĭ-mĭj). A long, weary journey, as to a shrine

pil'lag-ers (pĭl'ĭj-ērz). Plunderers

plied (plīd). To sail regularly

po-lit'i-cal (pȯ-lĭt'ĭ-kăl). Of or pertaining to the conduct of government

posed (pōzd). Pretended to be

pos'se (pŏs'ė). An armed band; a force with legal authority

po'ten-cy (pō-tĕn-sĭ). Quality of strength

pre-dict' (prė-dĭkt'). Foretell; prophesy

pre-lim'i-na'ries (prė-lĭm'ĭ-nė'-rĭz). A preparatory measure

pres'er-va'tion (prĕz'ēr-vā'-shŭn). Keeping from destruction, intact

pre-sid'i-o (prė-sĭd'ĭ-ō). A Spanish fort

pre-sum'a-bly (prė-zūm'ȧ-b'lĭ). Acting on a hunch or belief

prey (prā). To make raids for the sake of booty; to seize

pri'va-teer' (prī'vȧ-tēr'). The commander of an armed private vessel commissioned to cruise against the commerce or war vessels of the enemy

pro-cure' (prȯ-kūr'). Get; obtain

prom'i-nent (prŏm'ĭ-nĕnt). Standing out; notable

pro-pri'e-ty (prȯ-prī'ė-tĭ). The observance of a rule or code or a sense of what is fitting

pug-na'cious (pŭg-nā'shŭs). Disposed to fight

R.

ra'cial (rā'shăl). Of a race or family of men

ran'dom (răn'dŭm). Without aim or direction

rat'i-fied (răt'ĭ-fīd). Formally approved

ra'tion (rā'shŭn). An allowance; share

re-al'i-ty (rė-ăl'ĭ-tĭ). The character of being true to life

re'as-sur'ing (rē'ȧ-sŭr-ĭng). Assuring again

re-birth' (rē-bûrth'). A second birth; revival

re-cessed' (rė-sĕst'). Set back

re-cip'ro-cate (rė-sĭp'rȯ-kāt). To return in kind or degree

326

Glossary

re-cruit' (rḛ-krōōt). A newly enlisted soldier, sailor, or marine

re-lease' (rḛ-lēs'). To let go

rem'nant (rĕm'nănt). Remainder

re-mote' (rḛ-mōt'). Situated at a distance; out of the way

ren'der (rĕn'dēr). To melt down

ren'e-gade (rĕn-ḛ-gād'). Deserter; traitor

res'er-va'tion (rĕz'ēr-vā'-shŭn). A tract of the public land reserved for some special use

re-source'ful-ness (rḛ-sōrs'-fŏŏl-ness). Having great resources

re-sour'ces (rḛ-sōr'sĕs). Wealth in money, property, products, etc.

re-stored' (rḛ-stōrd'). To put back into the original state

right'-of-way' (rīt'ŭv-wā'). The land occupied by a railroad for its tracks

ri'val-ry (rī'văl-rĭ). Competition

S.

sad'dle-girth' (sad'l-gûrth'). A band or a strap which encircles the body of a horse

sal'vage (săl'vĭj). To rescue or save from wreckage

sanc'tu-ar'y (săngk'tu̇-ẽr'ĭ). The most sacred part of any church building

sand'pip'er (sănd'pīp'ẽr). A bird resembling a plover and having a long soft bill

sat'u-rat'ed (săt'ṳ-rāt'ĕd). Thoroughly soaked with moisture

scar'ci-ty (skâr'sĭ-tĭ). Lacking in provision; want of provisions for the support of life

scoured (skourd). Passed swiftly over in search of something

scribe (skrīb). A copier of manuscripts

sed'i-ment (sĕd'ĭ-mĕnt). Material deposited by water

se-rene' (sḛ-rēn'). Calm

sex'ton (sĕks'tŭn). One who rings the church bell

shoat (shōt). A pig

sid'ings (sīd'ĭngs). Sidetracks

siege (sēj). Blockade

sig-nif'i-cance (sĭg-nĭf'ĭ-kăns). Meaning; importance

sil'ver-smith' (sĭl-vẽr-smĭth'). One who makes utensils, ornaments, etc., from silver

sim-plic'i-ty (sĭm-plĭs'-ĭ-tĭ). Quality or state of being simple; plainness

si'mul-ta'ne-ous (sī'mŭl-tā'nḛ-ŭs). Taking place at the same time

sin'ews (sĭn'ūs). Tendons; cords connecting muscle

sin'gu-lar (sĭng'gṳ-lẽr). Unusual; strange

site (sīt). The local position of

smith (smĭth). One who forges with a hammer

sock'et (sŏk'ĕt). An opening or hollow that forms a holder for something

so-journ' (sḛ-jŭrn'). To stay in a place for a short time

Glossary

sor'ghum (sôr'gŭm). Sirup from sorghum juice, rich in invert sugar

sov'er-eign (sŏv'ẽr-ĭn). A person, body of men, or state having highest power

sov'er-eign-ty (sŏv'ẽr-ĭn-tĭ). Supreme political power

spe'cies (spē'shĭz). A distinct sort of animal or plant

spec-ta'tor (spĕk-tā'tẽr). One who looks on

spin'dle (spĭn'd'l). A long thin rod used as a pin

spur (spûr). A projection of railroad track

stam'i-na (stăm'ĭ-nȧ). Vigor; capacity for enduring

stealth (stĕlth). Going in secret; a secret action

stop'page (stŏp'ĭj). Act of stopping

sty (stĭ). A pen for hogs

sub-or'di-nate (sŭ-bôr'dĭ-nĭt). That which belongs to a lower class

sub'si-dy (sŭb'sĭ-dĭ). A government grant of money

sub-sist'ence (sŭb-sĭs'tĕns). Living

su'per-sti'tious (sū-pẽr-stĭsh'ŭs). Believing in, fearing or reverencing the unknown or mysterious

sure'ty (shŏŏr'tĭ). Security; guarantee

sur-vive' (sẽr-vīv'). To remain alive

sur-vi'vors (sẽr-vī'vẽrs). Those who live longer than the others

swash'buck'ler (swŏsh-bŭk'lẽr). A boasting soldier

T.

tac'tic (tăk'tĭk). A way of or device for doing something

tar-pau'lin (tär-pô'lĭn). Waterproofed canvas used for a covering

tend'er (tĕn'dẽr). A boat for communicating between shore and a larger vessel

ter'mi-nus (tûr'mĭ-nŭs). End; limit

thresh'old (thrĕsh'ōld). Entrance; door

ties (tīz). Cross supports to which railroad rails are fastened

toll'ing (tōl'ĭng). Ringing

tract (trăkt). An area not definitely bounded

tra-di'tion (trȧ-dĭsh'ŭn). Something handed down from the past

trait (trāt). A distinguishing quality or character

trap'pings (trăp'pĭngs). Ornaments

trea'son (trē'z'n). The betrayal of any trust or confidence

treas'ur-y (trĕzh'ẽr-ĭ). The place of deposit and disbursement of funds

trib'u-tar'y (trĭb'ȧ-tẽr'ĭ). A stream flowing into a larger stream or other body of water

U.

un'af-fect'ed (ŭn'ȧ-fĕk'tĕd). Natural; genuine

un-char'ted (ŭn-chär'tĕd). Not

328

Glossary

mapped

un′der-pro-vi′sioned (ŭn′dẽr-prŏ-vĭzh′ŭnd). Lacking in provisions, especially food

un′in-hab′it-ed (ŭn′ĭn-hăb′ĭtĕd). Not lived in

un-var′nished (ŭn-vär′nĭsht). Not varnished; plain

V.

val′id (văl′ĭd). Founded on truth or fact; sound

ver′dict (vûr′dĭkt). Decision

ver′sion (vûr′shŭn). An account or description from a particular point of view

vice′roy (vīs′roi). The governor of a country or province who rules as the representative of his king or sovereign

vi-cin′i-ty (vĭ-sĭn′ĭ-tĭ). Neighborhood

vi′cious (vĭsh′ŭs). Wicked

vir′tu-al-ly (vûr′tụ-ăl-lĭ). Being in effect but not in fact

W.

wards (wôrds). Persons who are under protection

way′bill′ (wā′bĭl′). A document issued with every shipment of freight, giving details regarding the goods, route, and charges

wheel′wright′ (hwēl′rīt′). A man whose occupation is to make or repair wheels or wheeled vehicles

wil′y (wīl′ĭ). Cunning; crafty

Guide to Pronunciation

ā as in lāte	ē as in wē	ō as in ōld	ŭ as in ŭs
ă as in ăm	ê as in ê nough	ô as in ȯ bey′	û as in bûrn
â as in câre	ĕ as in wĕt	ŏ as in nŏt	o͞o as in mo͞on
ȧ as in ȧsk	ē as in or′dēr	ô as in hôrse	o͝o as in fo͝ot
ä as in ärm	ī as in hīde	ū as in ūse	oi as in oil
â as in al′wâys	ĭ as in hĭd	ụ as in ụnite′	ou as in out

To the Teacher

To the Teacher:

As you know, reading abilities and interests of children in the intermediate grades cover a wide range, this range often extending from the fourth to the tenth grade.

It is true, also, that reading *materials* for children in the intermediate grades show a great range and variety.

A prominent educator has recently pointed out that the areas in which demands for increased reading skill in intermediate grades will be made, are:

First: Children should continue to enjoy recreational material, but their reading should include many different types of fiction, poetry, biography, and informational material. As they read more widely, they should become more discriminating in their tastes. They can be expected to develop standards for evaluating what they read, to become interested in special authors and illustrators, and to enjoy different writing styles.

Second: There should be much wider use of informational materials. In the intermediate grades these include textbooks to a much greater extent than they did earlier. In many schools children will work with five or six books in a given subject-matter area rather than with a single adopted text. Standard encyclopedias, atlases, almanacs, and other compilations should be used more frequently. The more mature children should also be able to follow much of the news in the daily paper, to locate articles in current magazines, and to read pamphlets. Of all the new demands made on older children, those occasioned by this greatly increased variety of informational materials are likely to be among the heaviest.

To the Teacher

Third: Intermediate-grade children should show increased skill in evaluating what they read in terms of their purposes. In recreational reading this should result in wider acquaintance with authors and illustrators, in increased sensitivity to differences in writing style, and in increased insight in selecting books for varied purposes. In informational reading intermediate-grade children should be able to make more discriminating decisions regarding the appropriateness of material to their problems. Perhaps more important, they should be able to handle more complex problems of appraising the accuracy of what they read—deciding how to check when textbooks disagree; determining a writer's qualifications; distinguishing between editorial writing and news reporting; distinguishing fact from fiction.[1]

The stories in this book may be used to enrich the reading experiences of your class in the following ways:

(1) As supplementary reading for the entire class or for small groups.

(2) As a source of information for small groups within the class who are working upon problems in social studies.

(3) For the personal reading of children who are interested in the history of the Southwest.

The stories in this book are intended, also, to enrich and expand the content usually found in textbooks in social studies and in basal readers. A few selections, written by persons who lived at or near the time the events occurred, were taken di-

[1]Margaret McKim, *Guiding Growth in Reading* (New York: The Macmillan Co., 1955), p. 318.

To the Teacher

rectly from their original sources. The language used is that of the authors except in rare cases where necessary to simplify for children. The folk tales were included to help children understand the primitive peoples of the Southwest. Other stories are "historical fiction;" that is, they were placed in their true historical settings with fictional plots and characters.

The poems have been selected because they give added appreciation for the stories in the sections in which they are placed. They may be shared with the entire class through oral reading. Some of these poems may be adapted for choral reading and enjoyed by the total group.

The *Things to Do* at the end of each story are suggestions for activities that may help children meet some of the demands of reading in intermediate grades. They may be used in presenting the stories, or they may be used as aids to the interpretation of the selections.

Two specific things were kept in mind as the activities were planned:

(1) The problems suggested require the use of reading skills that the children need: evaluating what is read; organizing and summarizing materials; and interpreting graphs, maps, and charts.

(2) Provision was made for children to use the materials in creative ways. Reading about a subject is not enough to make learning effective; materials from stories have to be used in creative ways to become the child's own. Therefore, dramatization, making of movies, TV shows, maps, and illustrations were suggested often.

To the Teacher

In selecting for the glossary the words and meanings unique to the stories, and in order to avoid the use of words too difficult for the respective grade levels, well-known vocabulary studies were consulted. Because of the great differences in the abilities of children to attack words and the wide range in reading vocabularies, it was difficult to select the words for the glossary. Only the uncommon and seemingly more difficult words are presented. No attempt was made to meet the vocabulary needs of all children. Individual children should be encouraged to use dictionaries for words not included in the glossary.

It is the hope of the authors that, besides contributing to greater reading achievement, this book will give to children who use it a deeper understanding of our country's present through its attempt to make the past come alive. Also, it is their hope that children may find increased insight into their own problems by an understanding of the people in earlier times and places.

Acknowledgments

The authors and publishers wish to express their grateful thanks to all who have assisted in the preparation of the material in this book — for their constructive criticism, for assistance in reading proof, and for otherwise helping in editorial and artwork.

Also, to the following organizations and persons who have graciously permitted the use of material, they gratefully acknowledge their obligation: DAILY MEDITATION for *Phantom Bell* and *Sculptor of San José*; GAMMEL's BOOK STORE for *French Villagers on the Texas Frontier,* and *Overland Freight* by August Santleben, and *Life in a Frontier Town in 1858* by W. W. Mills; to MY COUNSELLOR for *Narrow Escape* by Frank Gholson; to TRUE WEST for *Maximilian's Gold;* to FRONTIER TIMES for *Longhorns* and *Southern Overland Mail;* to Ruby Terrill Lomax for *The Zebra Dun* and *Whoopee Ti Yi Yo — Git Along Little Dogies;* to Berta Hart Nance for *Cattle;* to THE CATTLEMAN for *Lost, Five Thousand Cattle;* to the PANHANDLE PLAINS HISTORICAL REVIEW and COLUMBIA PUBLICATIONS for *Gail Land Rushes;* to BLUE BOOK for *Crush, Texas;* to DAVID McKAY COMPANY for *Overland Stage* from THE WILD WILD WEST by James Daugherty, copyright 1948; to E. DeGolyer for *Across Aboriginal America — The First Englishmen in Texas;* to THE DAUGHTERS OF THE REPUBLIC OF TEXAS for *Flag Song of Texas* by Mrs. Lee C. Harby; to PARENTS INSTITUTE for *The Defense of Big Sandy;* to THE DEPARTMENT OF PUBLIC SAFETY for *A Texas Ranger Story;* and to SCRIPTURE PRESS, INC. for *A Real Cowboy.*